Playful Pen

A Collection of Lighthearted Short Stories

Lidia Hidalgo

ISBN: 978-0-692-92910-0

Cover art by Debbie Perez-Stable

Copyedited and formatted by Laura Handley

Acknowledgements

I dedicate this book with gratefulness to the memory of Jackie Green and to Carole Calladine. These talented and generous writers started the writing group at the Rocky River Senior Center, encouraged me to write, and helped me to become a better writer.

My love and heartfelt gratitude to my niece, Elena Handley, who prodded me into publishing these short stories and gifted me with their publication, and to her daughter, Laura Handley, who edited and formatted this book.

And a huge thank you to Debbie Perez-Stable, artist and fellow writer, for contributing the front cover art.

Contents

Written words:

We remember

our favorite ones, the renditions that have

reached deep into our souls and connected,

dancing with the same rhythm as our spirits,

staying with us for a lifetime.

--Lidia Hidalgo

Life Is Not Fair
(Remembering my pal Bob Moyer)

Life is not fair. A lot of people say this, but most of them have no idea how unfair life is. I know this statement is true, I really know.

You see, I have a very bad reputation, but I do not deserve it, really. Children are afraid of me, and young women always refer to me in derogatory terms. And for what? Just because of some silly fairy tale. There are absolutely no grounds to condemn me. I would like you to listen to me for a while. I will tell you my story, and then you can be the judge.

I am a wolf. I had lived a tranquil life in my home in the woods, doing the things proper to my species. Then, once upon a time, while I was minding my own business in the woods, I noticed a pretty, young girl, wearing a red coat and hood. Who wears red, I ask you? Only a person who wants to be noticed, I tell you.

Continuing my story, not only was this girl wearing red to attract my attention, but she was the one who stopped me and started chatting with me. She told me that she was on her way to take some food to her grandmother because the old woman was sick.

After the child and I talked for a while, she continued picking flowers to make a bouquet for her grandmother. Being the polite, gentle wolf that I am, I decided to pay the sick woman a visit, just to see if she needed anything. A neighborly gesture of goodwill, you know.

I have always been a fast walker, so in no time at all I arrived at the grandmother's house. I knocked on the door in a very well-mannered way, and entered only after I heard her say, "Please come in, the door is unlocked."

When I went inside, I found the woman in bed. Her eyesight must not have been very good, because she thought I was her granddaughter and asked me to get closer to the bed. Before getting sick, she must have been preparing some very tasty food,

3

since she smelled not of cologne or perfume but of delicious baked treats. By now, it was well past my lunchtime. The chat in the woods had caused me to miss my lunch. Since I never have breakfast, I was ravenous.

So, when the grandmother said, "Please, make yourself at home. If you are hungry, eat anything you may find around," what was I supposed to do? If I refused her invitation to eat, I would have offended her. So, in order not to hurt her feelings, I politely said, "Thank you," and looked around for some food. Once again, my olfactory sense brought me back to her. I decided to comply with her invitation, and I ate her up.

Then I thought of how disappointed her granddaughter was going to be to come all this way and not find her grandmother, so in order to not upset her, I dressed as the old woman and decided to rest for a while in bed while I digested my delicious lunch.

Finally, the slowpoke girl came in. She must have inherited her grandmother's bad eyesight, because she mistook me for her. She started by telling me, "Grandma, what big eyes you have!"

I replied, "The better to see you with, my dear."

Then came "What big ears you have!"

My answer was, "The better to hear you with, dear child."

And finally, "What big teeth you have!"

Now, in all honesty, what is a well-bred wolf to do? The only correct answer was, "The better to eat you with!" So that was my answer, and even though I was not all that hungry anymore, I did not want to make the girl feel she was unappetizing, so I ate her up.

I have heard that in some versions of this fairy tale, there is a hunter who comes and kills me. Since I am the one telling you this story, you can guess that, as Mark Twain once said, "Reports of my death have been greatly exaggerated." When the hunter came, he ended up as my dessert.

Now that you have heard my story, don't you agree with me? I have been the subject of unfair, very bad publicity. I am just a very polite wolf who did not want to hurt other people's feelings.

I have been kind of lonely lately. Would like to pay me a visit? I have not had my lunch yet, and my manners continue to be impeccable.

Alliteration

I like and am lured by language
laden with the limpid, lively sound of *l*'s.
Lifted from my languid lethargy,
lacking in labor, left with leisure,
liberated from a litany of literary lessons,
in lieu of rules, licensed to play.
Light of spirit,
lifted of strain,
with a lather of levity,
this lucky lady called Lidia
will likely laden and lace the page,
littering it with a largess of letter *l*'s.
Launched like lava,
lavender in color,
and lilac in scent,
I'll lavish *l*'s on the lines,
laying a large list.
L's leap from my lips and lay down
like leaves leaving a ledge,
landing on the tablet in my lap.
Given this liberty to launch,
I now look at a limitless legion of *l*'s
looming, lurching and loitering.
But, to avoid listless listeners,
sensing the limit of your patience in sight,
feeling liable to lose my life,
I'll limit my lark of lyric pursuit,
this lack of lucidity,
and laughing at my loony quest,
I'll simply say "Later!"

Do Not Fear, the Butler Is Here

Mrs. Simpson went to Europe every year. She enjoyed spending her summers abroad. Her husband had been dead now for ten years. He had started as a salesman, but had founded his own company and had eventually become a very wealthy man. The Simpsons had not had any children.

Mrs. Simpson's house had been featured in several magazines. It had been designed by a very well-known architect and decorated without taking the cost into consideration. It was indeed a beautiful place, and contained a great number of artworks that truly belonged in a museum.

Mr. Jones, the new butler, had been hired just before Mrs. Simpson left on her trip. She was a little concerned about leaving a new person in charge of her estate for such a long time, but the butler, who seemed to be a very calm person, had assured her that she did not have anything to fear. He would take very good care of everything.

A few days after her arrival in England, Mrs. Simpson decided to call home and make sure everything was all right. She placed the call and was beginning to wonder why the butler was taking so long to answer the phone when she heard his voice. "Mrs. Simpson's residence."

"Hello, Jones. It's me, Mrs. Simpson. How are things going?"

"Do not worry, ma'am, everything is just fine. There is just a little something you should know, though. Remember the scarf you left on top of the sofa in the den?"

"Yes?" answered the caller.

"Well, ma'am, I hate to tell you that you will not be able to wear it anymore."

"How come?"

"Cindy, your puppy, took it in her mouth and ran all over the house with it."

7

Mrs. Simpson was annoyed, since she loved that silk scarf, but she was not going to let such a minor thing spoil her good mood. "Too bad," she replied, "but don't worry about it."

"I did try my very best to stop the puppy. I ran after her. As a matter of fact, Giant, the Saint Bernard, helped me. He also ran after Cindy, trying to get the scarf, but to no avail."

"That's OK, Mr. Jones. Is everything else all right?"

"Yes, ma'am, except that you should also know that when Giant and I ran after Cindy, he bumped the floor lamp in the foyer, and it fell to the floor and broke."

This time, the lady's face showed a momentary frown. The lamp had been a wedding present from her aunt, and it had been very expensive. Oh well, she thought, I can afford to replace it. "Anything else I should know?"

"Perhaps one more thing, ma'am. When the lamp fell and broke, it injured Whiskers, your black cat, who was lying on the floor next to it."

Mrs. Simpson's face turned serious again. She loved her cat. She tried to remain calm as she said "Would you explain further, please?"

"Whiskers was so upset by the sudden noise and the cuts he sustained that he ran very fast and overturned the little table with the small ashtray on top. The ashtray also broke."

The news was almost a relief. "That's fine. I've always hated that ashtray. Any other news?"

"Well…" He hesitated for a moment. "I guess you should know that your canary died."

"Oh!" said the pet owner in a very concerned voice, for she cared deeply for all her pets. "How did that happen?"

"It's easy to explain. See, it was also the result of the ashtray falling down."

"How come?" asked Mrs. Simpson with an edge to her voice. An uncomfortable feeling welled up in the pit of her stomach. "What happened?"

A moment later came the explanation. "The table bumped his cage and made it fall also. He was OK after the fall, but neither he, Whiskers, Cindy, nor Giant survived what followed."

With one hand over her rapidly beating heart and the other trying to dry the perspiration on her forehead, she cried, "My dear pets! What do you mean? What have you not told me?"

"Just a small detail," said the butler slowly. "I was smoking when Cindy ran away with your scarf, and since I did not want to dirty your carpet with ashes, I put my cigar on the ashtray before I ran after her. When the ashtray fell, the cigar ignited the carpet."

"My Persian carpet got burn marks?" she screamed.

"Yes, ma'am" he calmly replied. "But don't worry, it ended up not mattering."

"How is that?" she yelled back, even louder now.

"Well, by the time the firemen arrived, it was too late. Everything burned down. The garage is OK, though. That is where I have been staying. And you'll be happy to know that the phone is working again."

As he pronounced these last words, the butler wondered what the loud thump he heard at the other end of the line was.

Matchmaking in Action

Name: John Smith. *I better not give my real name, just in case.*

Age: 35. *Everyone tells me I look a lot younger than my forty-nine years.*

Eye color: Hazel.

Hair color: Brown. *I'll use Just for Men before I meet anyone.*

Height: 6 ft. *I'm sure she won't bring a ruler on our first date and find out I'm really 5'6".*

Weight: 230, all muscle. *This is really true. I've been doing a lot of push-ups and have not drank beer for a long time.*

Education: High School. *Not really a lie, just a little stretch. I did go for a few months. Nobody needs to know I dropped out of high school in my freshman year.*

Profession: Handyman. *Hey, that sounds a lot better than car thief. And it's true that I'm good with my hands: I'm great at opening a car without a key and getting it moving.*

Hobbies: Motorcycle riding, playing basketball, and reading. *I'm not a fool: I won't include stealing cars and motorcycles, which are my main hobbies. The rest is true. In the last three years, I did play a little basketball with the other inmates, and I read all the writing on the walls of my cell during my most recent stint at the state penitentiary.*

I would like to meet a pretty young woman with similar interests for a friendly relationship that could lead to something more serious. *I've been told I won't get many replies unless I say I'm interested in a permanent relationship, so here it goes. That's not a problem for me. I'm pretty good at making myself scarce later on.*

Name: Mary Brown. *Better that they don't find out who I really am in case my date turns out to be a policeman and remembers booking me the last time I went shopping and forgot to pay. As I tried to explain to that cute young policeman who arrested me, anybody can have a memory lapse, and I just happen to have them often when I shop.*

Age: 28. *Sounds much better than 45. Everyone expects women to take off a few years, so seventeen less is not too many.*

Eye color: Blue. *No need to mention my colored contact lenses.*

Hair color: Blonde. *Thanks, Clairol!*

Height: 5'4".

Weight: 120. *Let's hope that girdle I saw advertised does its job on my 160 pounds!*

Education: College. *I did take a cosmetology course for a few weeks years ago, and nobody is going to ask to see my diploma.*

Profession: Hairdresser. *He doesn't need to know that I don't work and am looking for someone to do it for me.*

Hobbies: Dancing, reading. *I do read my horoscope every day.*

I would like to meet a worthwhile young man for friendship only. *I can always nag him into a more serious relationship later on, but I don't want to scare away any possible candidates now.*

I am unattached and free as a bird. *I can ask Rosie to babysit my three kids while I go on a date. He doesn't need to find out about them yet.*

Now the fun begins!

What Would You Say to an Uninvited Guest?

I am throwing a party tonight at my place. I am glad I have everything ready on time, since my first guests are ringing the doorbell.

We are having a swell time. Everyone I invited has come to this informal gathering. I am very fond of all my friends.

An hour into the party, I see a newcomer arrive, and my friend John welcomes him in. I am sure that John thinks this stranger is a friend of mine, but I do not know this person. I have good reason to believe that he is crashing my party.

I work my way to him and, with drinks in our hands, we begin a conversation. After a couple of minutes, in a conspiratorial voice, I say "Let me tell you a secret. I do not know anybody here—I am crashing this party."

Buoyed by my confidence, he replies, "I'll have to confess that I am doing the same. I passed by, saw the cars, and figured I would stop by and have a few free drinks and perhaps steal a silver ashtray."

Without missing a beat I take him by his arm, walk him to the front door, and say, "I'll advise you to get those drinks at the bar of your preference. Too bad they won't be free, and the ashtray will not be silver."

All A's, E's, I's, O's, and U's

"¡Ay, Ay, Ay!" Or, as it is in English, "Ugh! Am I able?" Am I insane enough? Am I accepting, engaging in, and obediently attacking another incredible, inane assignment?

Actually, input another aspect, enjoyment, and instantaneously I optimistically assert, "All aboard! Onward!" I am elated! Once again, I experiment, embark on, and experience an almost innate act of embarrassment, abasement, and also enrapture, as I eagerly initiate and attempt an enterprise above any existent ability. It is as if I always aspired accomplishments of inhumane, unfeasible undertakings. Is anyone interested in observing and analyzing?

At expense of annoying and exasperating any or all in our audience, I'll add on, and I imagine I'll eventually efficiently extricate and end abruptly as I arrive at an inference. I am absolving our educator of any and all abuse, as once again, an assignment is an enticing escape, evoking utmost amusement and also awe, acclaim, applause, and utter admiration of instructor. If I outlive in abashment enunciating our intentionally ugly, unbearable, and unforgivable overdose of A's, E's, I's, O's, and U's, I ought obliteration of any additional extraordinary indictment. Instead, as, accidentally, I achieve, end, and accomplish our undertaking, as always, I eagerly anticipate, encourage, and endorse announcement of an encore. I'll incur again in an idiotic extravaganza on another occasion!

LIDIA HIDALGO

My New Wings

There is a first time for everything. It is a beautiful summer day, and I am on a high hill next to the ocean, getting ready to do something I've always dreamt of doing. I have with me my brand-new hang gliding equipment. That triangular piece of yellow nylon over an aluminum frame is going to give me the wings I've always wished for. I am very excited, perhaps a little nervous, but my overriding feeling is one of joy.

As I begin to run down the green grassy hill, my yellow wings are buffeted by the wind, and my feet rise slightly from the ground. As I get to the end of the hill, there is an anxious moment when I wonder if my new wings will really sustain me. I am delighted to see that they do, and I get into my horizontal position, grabbing the frame with both hands. At first, my knuckles are white from holding on so hard, but little by little I relax. I continue to hold firmly, but in a much softer manner.

The cool breeze caresses my face as I soar through the air. I am almost sorry to be wearing the required helmet. I would love to feel my hair floating in the wind! The sensation I feel is indescribable. My body has become weightless. I am being carried like a feather on the wind. I become one with my surroundings. I am a bird, but my flight requires less effort. I don't even need to flap my wings: the wind propels me, and very subtle shifts of my body control where I am going.

I look down to the gorgeous blue ocean. From this distance, the sparkling white crests of the waves are even more beautiful. There are many sailboats taking advantage of today's gentle breeze. Their multicolored sails speckle the water like confetti.

A flock of seagulls join me for a little while. They must wonder what this strange big yellow bird is, but very soon they realize I am no threat, and they continue their flight at my side and make mine even more enjoyable.

After some time I decide to drift a little lower. When I do, I can distinctly see some people on the beach looking at me and pointing up to the sky in my direction. A group of children run across the sand, attempting the impossible task of keeping up with me.

14

I return to a higher altitude and continue delighting in my ride in the sky for a very long time. This is the most relaxing and wonderful experience of my whole life. Eventually, I gradually lower myself until I touch down on a deserted portion of the beach. As I get out of my equipment, I think that I will repeat this marvelous experience as often as I can. I also know that, for the rest of my life, I will remember the first time that I sprouted wings.

Tabloid Article: Boy with Static-Electricity Disease Sparks Major Fire

Hiram (known to everyone as Hi) Voltage, a nine-year-old boy who suffers from a devastating and mysterious disease, was the cause of a major fire in his hometown of Burns, PA yesterday. Hi has lived with static-electricity disease for a couple of years now. The doctors don't understand how he acquired it. One theory is that it could have been from the time when, as a Boy Scout, he learned how to start a fire by rubbing two sticks together.

The unfortunate Hi is the object of constant ridicule from many of his classmates, since his hair is always standing up. Mrs. Voltage says that when the weather is too dry, she keeps him at home to try to avoid incidents like the one that happened yesterday. Burns had not seen rain for a few weeks, and the atmosphere was very dry.

Yesterday afternoon, unbeknownst to his mother, Hi decided to go to the small general store to buy a bottle of pop. As he arrived, his hair must have accidentally brushed against the curtain at the front window. Nobody realized the spark had started a fire until it was too late. The flames engulfed and devoured not only the store but several of the houses close by.

The small town is in an uproar. Some people wanted to kill the boy right then and there, but his relatives were able to restrain the agitated ones. There is a meeting tonight to request an ordinance prohibiting Hi from leaving his house unless it is a rainy or very humid day.

We have heard from reliable sources that a world-renowned scientist, an expert in this terrible disease, has come up with a new treatment. It consists of a shower-cap-like device that constantly provides drops of water to the head. We hope that research will prove this a worthwhile invention so that in the future, this pitiful young boy may be saved from his misery.

The author of this article is starting a fund to enable Hi to buy this invention once it becomes available. I am appealing to your sense of goodness, so please send all the money you have to:

Very Greedy

123 Hoax Rd

Swindle, CA 93111

In case you want to contact me in the future, I want to let you know that in about six months I plan to take an extended vacation to Bora Bora.

Who is Following You?

As I am walking home from my workout at the Y this late summer afternoon, I have the feeling I'm being followed. It is the same as when you sense rather than see that someone is staring at you, and then you look, and you were right, someone has been staring at you.

Not wanting to look straight back and let my follower know that I am aware of his presence, I continue walking at a leisurely pace. Yes, I realize that I said "his" presence, and that is because not only am I hoping it is a guy, but in my mind's eye I see him as a tall and handsome fellow. Perhaps the Adonis I saw lifting weights while I was on the exercise bike.

I just have several blocks to go. When is he going to make his move, catch up with me, and engage me in conversation? Oh, please let it not be one of those creeps that bother beautiful young women like me.

I am now on my last block. I can see my house. The good news is that if he attempts anything inappropriate, I can just run inside. The bad news is that if he does not make his move in the next few seconds, it might just have been that someone was coincidentally following the same route as me.

I take my house key out. Just as I am opening the door, so I'll feel safe if it turns out to be a pervert, I turn my head to look at my pursuer. Even though it is not the handsome guy I had imagined, I am not too disappointed. His large, beautiful, warm brown eyes and happily wagging tail tells me that we are going to be in love forever.

Tick Tock Tick Tock

Tick tock, tick tock, tick tock, the big clock on my nightstand sings loudly, without mercy. Its annoying melody prevents me from falling asleep. I have tried everything I can think of, except maybe earplugs, which I don't have. I pulled the sheet, blanket, and pillow over my head. I moved my tired body as far as possible from the offending clock. Nothing seems to help. I can't take this irritating device to another room, as I would like to, since I need its alarm to wake me up tomorrow at the crack of dawn so I can get ready for work.

I resign myself to a sleepless night when suddenly, the tick tock of the clock is dwarfed by an even louder noise somewhere else in the house. No longer do I hear the tick tock; now all my ears perceive is a strange noise coming from who knows where. At first it sounds like a thump. Perhaps someone came in through a window? (Did I leave one open?) Then it sounds more like a rustle, like someone trying not to make too much noise as they invade my home. Oh! Give me that nice soft tick tock lullaby, I plead. I like it much better than what I am hearing now. Why didn't I join the softball team at work when I was asked? I need a bat under my bed!

What else can I use? My cell phone is too small. The clock, the one that just moments ago seemed so big and loud, is really very small, now that I look at it. It would not inflict much damage, and it certainly wouldn't deter an intruder. I have a pen and some paper over there. Make a paper plane and fly it at him to scare him away? No, I don't think that would work. Well, I guess I could at least write my last will and testament, just in case.

Hey, no negative thinking, girl, let's be positive! Could this be my opportunity to meet my significant other? Fat chance—I don't want to get involved with a burglar. There MUST be something positive about this mess that I'm in!

Well, let me be brave and try to scare away the intruder. If I succeed, they will probably interview me for the six o'clock news. (And if I don't, I'll BE the news!) OK, I will succeed. I will scare him off! And I'll be sure to buy a new outfit to wear to the press

19

conference tomorrow. Who knows, maybe my prince charming will be watching the news...

With these encouraging thoughts in mind, I silently get up and grab the latest science fiction book from the nightstand, the one I was reading just before closing my eyes. It's a heavy book. It might do the trick, if I hit him right on the head. I walk stealthily towards the living room, where the noise seems to be coming from. With my right hand held high, clutching my makeshift weapon, I use my other hand to turn on the light and scare off my enemy. To my surprise, all I hear is a very loud and startled MEOW!

What are you doing here Milo? I thought I locked you up for the night in your private quarters in the basement. How did you get out?

Well, I guess I won't be needing a new outfit for tomorrow. Back to that obnoxious tick tock!

Choosing a Kitten

"Is today the day?" asked six-year-old Lizzy.

"Yes, today is the day you get your kitten."

Father and daughter got into the car, and Mark drove his young daughter to his cousin's home so she could choose a kitten.

When the door opened, Mark said, "Hi Tom. Lizzy is ready to pick up her kitten."

"Come in. I'll take you to where they are."

The sight of the mother cat and the big litter of kittens delighted both father and daughter.

"I'll let you play with them for a while before choosing," said Mark as he walked with Tom toward the living room.

The little girl played happily with the litter of kittens, giggling and squealing.

After visiting with his cousin, Mark came back to Lizzy.

"Can I name them?" asked the young girl.

"You can name what you take home. Tom will name the rest."

"How many can I take?" was her next question.

"You can take just one."

"With an impish look on her face, picking up two little kittens, Lizzy said, "This is 'Just' and this is 'One.'"

Mark was both shocked and proud at his daughter's quick thinking. Oh, my, he thought. What can I expect when she becomes a teenager? After a moment, he smiled and replied, "OK, you can take both."

With a twinkle in her eyes, and a smile on her lips, Lizzy picked up a third kitten and said, "This is 'Both.'"

Regretting His Fifteen Minutes of Fame

Today, Michael decided to go to his favorite restaurant for lunch. It was a small, out-of-the-way place that he could not visit too often. He really enjoyed both the food and the atmosphere there.

As he expected, he had a wonderful lunch. When he was done and decided to settle the bill, he had the surprise of his life. The owner of the restaurant came to see him in person. With a smile on his face, the owner said, "You happen to be our ten thousandth customer."

"Your lunch is free," said the owner, while a newspaper photographer took a picture of the two of them.

Michael did not have a smile on his face. All he could think was, "What will my boss's reaction be? I'm supposed to be home, sick in bed with the flu."

Doing Everything by the Book

My name is Mike, I am in my early thirties, and I live in New York City. I have always done everything by the book. I don't like to brag, but it is a fact that I move in the highest circles of society. Almost every week, I am invited to parties by the some of the best-known people in New York—well, really, in the world. My personal fortune keeps increasing.

People who have known me for a while know of my great wealth and also of my philanthropic work. When someone meets me for the first time, they may ask what business I am in. I tell them truly of my varied interests but also that my main focus is jewelry.

When I say that I have always done everything by the book, the only thing I neglect to mention is which book am I referring to. If you promise to keep my revelation confidential, I will tell you. When I was about twenty-five years old, I loved cats and even had one at my apartment, so the title of the book "How to Become a Cat Burglar Without Being Caught," attracted me. The subject turned out to not have anything to do with cats, but it gave my life a very lucrative direction.

Homophones

I had planned to go golfing with my friend Carol right after we drank our mid-morning *teas*. I was sure she would *tease* me because I am such a bad golf player. But when we arrived at the club, they were out of *tees*, so we had to wait for another group of players to finish before we could start.

Since the day was *chilly*, we decided to have something hot to eat. Being originally from *Chile* and having lived in Mexico, Carol convinced me to have a *chili* plate that was too spicy for my taste.

I should have had enough *sense* not to order it and to spend my *cents* on an old-fashioned ham sandwich, but I have to admit that the *scents* coming from the kitchen seduced me to try the foreign dish.

Why the Customer Is Never Right

Why is the customer never right? I'll tell you why.

I have worked as a sales clerk for my whole adult life. Let me give you just a few examples of what some of those precious customers have done.

An ugly older woman comes to me with the following complaint: "I want to return this beauty cream I bought two weeks ago."

"Why?" I ask her.

"It doesn't work!" she answers.

Trying to rein in what my tongue wants to tell her, I just say, "One moment please," while I work on the exchange receipt. All the while, I am thinking, "What did you expect? Did you think you were going to look exactly like the twenty-five-year-old actress who advertises this product on TV?"

And don't think that it is only women who buy the wrong things.

Another customer, a man this time, well past his prime, comes to exchange a cologne that did not achieve the promised results with the members of the opposite sex. Once again, time to keep my mouth shut, but I do wish, oh so much, to tell him "There is no product on the market that would make a cute young girl fall in love with you!"

What about the customer who buys a beautiful dress in size five when she knows perfectly well that she really needs something more than four times bigger? Sometimes I don't know how I keep a straight face.

I have to smile and act as if, of course, the product was defective, and after the exchange, even say, "Thank you, and please come again," while I am truly hoping that I will never see her face again.

Sun Is Rising From Its Sleep (140 Characters)

Sun is rising from its sleep

So must I without a peep

Outside so cold and snowy

Bed so warm and cozy

Bright idea:

    Fake cough, call boss, goof off

My New Car

I am so happy! I just bought a brand-new car. Wait until you hear this. It is delivering itself to my driveway. I hear it clicking my garage door opener (which I had left at the car dealership for them to connect to my car) and the car parks itself perfectly inside the garage. Wow! It does not even forget to close the garage door after it is inside. Isn't that wonderful? I can't wait to take it for a ride, or rather, for it to take me for a ride.

I have a lot to do tonight—I have to prepare dinner, and some of my friends are coming over for a meeting in an hour—so I'll have to wait until tomorrow morning to try out my car.

It is now morning. I could hardly sleep last night, I was so excited thinking about my new car. I even dreamt that on my first trip it flew me to the moon like a spaceship.

I have a light and quick breakfast since I cannot wait any longer. Then I take my smart phone and say, "Arthur, I want to go for a ride." As you might have guessed, Arthur is my new car's name.

A moment later, I hear the garage door go up. The car engine turns on, and the car backs up the driveway, stopping precisely at my back door. Then I see the garage door go down again. How thoughtful!

The car door opens by itself. I get in, the door closes automatically, and I am buckled in without my having to hunt for the seat belt. I then hear Arthur's very friendly voice say, "Good morning, Lidia. Where do you wish to go?"

Wanting to be as polite as Arthur, I reply, "Good morning Arthur. I would like to go to Huntington Beach, please."

"My pleasure, Lidia," it replies, and away we go.

I do not need to worry about other drivers, nor about braking, accelerating, red lights, green lights or anything else. Arthur takes care of everything. I can simply look out the windows and admire my surroundings, feeling sorry for the poor people who have to

27

take care of all those things by themselves. I enjoy every second of the twenty-minute ride.

Soon enough, we are at the Lake Road entrance to Huntington Beach. We go in, and before I realize it, Arthur is taking me down the steep stairs to the beach. Oops! Perhaps I should have been a little more specific: instead of saying that I wanted to go "to Huntington Beach," I should have said "to the parking lot at Huntington Beach." Well, it is too late now. Down the stairs we go. Does this car have a muffler? I hope it is not destroyed... I hear a lot of banging. What about its new tires? Even with the wonderful shock absorbers, I keep hitting my head against the car's ceiling. I'm beginning to get a bad headache.

Now we are on the sand. Arthur is not deterred by this and keeps forging forward until we are in the water.

"Whoa, Arthur!" I scream in spite of my throbbing head. "This is enough, please, stop! I did not bring my swimming suit!"

Right away the car stops, and a cheerful voice says, "Your wish is my command, Lidia."

I try to open the door and, with great effort, finally succeed in doing so. Some water gets inside, but I do want to get out of this darn car before it drowns me! I also forgot to tell Arthur that I don't know how to swim.

I am wet up to my knees. Slowly, I waddle out of the water and sit down on the sand to catch my breath.

A few feet away, I see Arthur, who seems to be enjoying the waves lapping over him.

What was I thinking when I bought this car? I should have my head examined. I hope I have enough money left in my savings account to buy myself a bicycle, since that will be my mode of transportation from now on!

End of the World

"END OF THE WORLD IS COMING IN TEN DAYS!" I read.

Though skeptical, I could not keep myself from continuing to read the flier that somebody had left on my front porch. My mind envisioned prophesies of calamities, of impending doom, of massive earthquakes and torrential rains, of atomic explosions. Not only my neighborhood, city, state, and country, but the whole world would disappear in a big poof, with only a void left in its stead! Although I tried to stay calm, I noticed my hand trembling a little and perspiration forming on my forehead. I took a deep breath and went to the kitchen, where I forced myself to have a drink of water before resuming reading.

As I continued, my apprehension was followed by some anger and some admiration too. The flier referred to the opening, in ten days, of a new restaurant and bar called The End of the World.

Hey, I won't wait for its opening day. I need that beer now!

If I …

If I flunk my algebra test one more time, I will be grounded for at least a month.

If I am grounded, I will not be able to attend Kate's birthday party.

If I can't go to Kate's party, I will miss my chance to see her and to try to get a date with her.

If I can't go out with Kate and give her the opportunity to get to know me outside of school, she will never go to the fall dance with me.

If I can't take Kate to the dance, I will have to take my younger sister Gayle.

If I end up having to take my sister to the dance, I will be the laughingstock of all my friends.

If all my friends make fun of me, I will be too self-conscious to impress the one person I want to impress, who is Kate.

I better hit the books right away. I don't want to fail my algebra test!

On second thought, I need to study, but I have to be careful not to overdo it. I could get an A+, but then my parents would find out that I can do that and will expect me to get only A's from now on. Life is so complicated! I need to make sure to get a C, nothing more, nothing less. Sounds like a good plan to me!

Little Dog

Mrs. Johnson inched toward me with her walker. The little creature she called a dog snarled.

"My dog has been acting strangely lately," she said. "For some reason, he doesn't bark like he used to. He still eats all his food, so he must not be sick, but I don't know what's wrong with him."

"And how are you doing, Mrs. Johnson?" I asked, trying to be polite.

"As well as can be expected at my age," she answered. "In a few days, I will have cataract surgery."

"And how is your heart?"

"My heart is pretty strong and healthy."

OK, I thought, so you will survive the shock of your life when you find out after your eye surgery that for the last couple of weeks, your pet has been a dirty rat. I wonder if the rat was so hungry that it ate your dear little Fifi or if Fifi was quick enough to escape.

Six-Word Stories

Made big mistake. Need new job.

Teenager crashes car. Now exercises plenty.

Parents on vacation. Police end party.

Cute puppy. No sleep. Darn dog!

Need bigger door or smaller sofa.

Started diet. Brownies to the garbage.

Retrieved brownies from garbage. Diet tomorrow.

No Thank You

"No thank you, I do not smoke." *I would much rather that you didn't in front of me, but, being in a public place, I can't tell you that.*

I don't know why I let myself be talked into meeting this guy. My friend Arlene is a born matchmaker, and she is always trying to set her friends up with members of the opposite sex.

"No, thank you, I already had dinner, and I am not hungry at all." *What a boring guy! I can't help being distracted, he just keeps going on and on about his work. I don't think Arlene realizes what a bore her acquaintance is.*

"No, thank you, I already saw that movie." *I am not lying, I did see it, but even if I had not, I would not go see a movie with you.*

"No, thank you, I have to get up very early for work tomorrow. I cannot go dancing with you now." *If you were less boring and better looking, I would not mind having just a few hours of sleep, but, of course, I can't tell you that.*

"No, thank you, I will be very busy the rest of the week, don't bother calling me. I'll let you know when my schedule lightens up." *For you, I'll be busy the rest of my life!*

Getting Old

Jonathan lived on a farm a good distance from the nearest city. The big, white farmhouse, just a few feet from a small lake, was home to a large family which included parents, grandparents, and six children, ranging in age from five-year-old Mark to sixteen-year-old Jane.

The Sears clan was a close-knit family. They got along fine. Each member knew what was expected of them as far as their work at the farm, and they did their assigned tasks to the best of their abilities.

As in any family, there were, at times, disagreements, but they were always solved by a very democratic majority vote, in which even the six children were included.

Jonathan was a happy fellow. Holidays got him down though. Usually around Thanksgiving and Christmas, he would get into one of his depressed moods.

Getting old was the most difficult thing Jonathan Sears had ever done. Last Thanksgiving, he had almost died, and he could not forget that. Even though he survived, he was left with great apprehension.

Did I mention that Jonathan is Mark's pet turkey? Last Thanksgiving he survived by just one vote. No wonder he would like the calendar to skip over the November and December holidays!

Message to Wife

Fred sent this message to his wife: "Susan, I am having one more beer with my pals."

"It's a good thing that my phone has a 'resend message' feature," said Fred to his best friend. "I'll probably use it several times tonight."

This reminded Fred of his friend Ryan who was a math teacher at a nearby school. One evening, Ryan went out with his friends. As he left, his wife asked him, "Are you going to be back late, dear?"

"I'll be back at a quarter of twelve," he replied.

"Oh, that's fine," said Ryan's wife.

She waited up for him, but a quarter of twelve came and went, and Ryan had not returned. She kept waiting for him, now a little worried. One o'clock, two o'clock, and no Ryan.

Finally, at three o'clock, he arrived.

"Why are you so late?" asked his concerned wife.

"Dear, I am exactly on time—or have you forgotten your fractions? I said I would be back at a quarter of twelve, and I am back, right on time, at three o'clock."

Now, Son, Do You Know What You Did Wrong?

"Now, son, do you know what you did wrong?" said the teacher to a young student in his class.

Tim, like most nine-year-olds, did not have any idea what he had done wrong, but he thought that if he admitted he did not know, he would make things much worse for himself. So he replied, "Yes, sir, and you can be sure that I will never do it again."

"But you are doing it again," answered his teacher.

"No, you have my word that I will not do it again," said Tim, who was getting more and more nervous by the minute, wondering what they were talking about.

"What is it that you will not do again?" asked the teacher in a firm voice.

"What you don't want me to keep doing," said the boy, trying to keep his cool without much success.

"What I don't want you to do is to pretend that you understand something when you don't," the teacher replied, almost at the end of his patience.

"Oh! Is that all? I'm relieved—I thought I had done something much worse."

The Polka Dot

My eyes were drawn to the polka dot.

What polka dot, you ask? It was a small, black polka dot that moved with purpose.

I followed it, intrigued as to its destination.

It traveled forward on a straight line and then, as if as an afterthought, zigzagged at an angle from its original path.

I could not take my attention from it. I admired its beauty. It seemed to be parading for my delight.

Then, recalling its ability to ascend, the black polka dot with the red background took flight, and the colorful ladybug disappeared from my view.

Transposed Letters

Helen was *making the tail* for the monkey costume that her son Greg was going to wear at his birthday party two weeks from now. Greg's birthday was the day before Halloween, so, as usual, the celebration would be a costume party. Helen was not only a skillful seamstress but also a very creative person; she enjoyed making costumes for her children. People always complimented her on her ingenious designs.

"How is my costume coming along, Mom?" Greg asked as soon as he got home from school.

"Come and see for yourself," answered Helen from the sewing room.

When Greg came into the room and saw the costume, a big smile appeared on his face. "Wow, Mom, it looks like a real monkey!"

"I told you it was going to be a good one," she replied.

Greg's fascination with monkeys had started at a young age, when his dad had read him one of the Curious George books. Later on, when Greg saw monkeys at the zoo, his love for the animals increased. He had all kinds of stuffed monkeys and a zillion books about them.

Once the tail was finished, the costume was ready. Then Helen addressed all the invitations to the party. It promised to be a fun event. *Taking the mail* to the post office was the very last step in the party preparations.

One-Syllable Story: The Last Time I Saw Her, She...

The last time I saw her, she was in one of her sad moods. She cried all the time. All seemed dark to her. I tried to cheer her up as best I could, but I failed to do so.

The next day, I had to leave town and was gone for a long time. When I came back, my first thought was to see how my friend was. I asked and was told that she was fine. She had met a rich guy.

I was pleased with the news and phoned her. "This is Max, I'm back from my trip," I said, and we talked for what seemed short to us but was a long time.

She was glad to hear from me and asked me to come see her, so I did. She seemed much changed.

"I know how great I have it. I do try to just see the good now," she told me. "Since I met Jim, my life is bliss, my blues are gone."

As fine as this news was, I sensed a glitch. "What's wrong? I asked in my straight way.

"Not much."

"Are you sure?"

"Jim is a good guy. He works hard and is rich and fun."

"What's wrong?" I asked once more.

She put her head in her hands. Tears ran down her cheeks as she said, "He drinks too much. When he does, he is not nice; he is mean."

"What will you do?"

"I want to leave as fast as I can! I don't care if he has a lot of dough. I can't stand that he hits me. Will you help me?"

"Of course I will. You are my friend, and I will help you."

And that was how the next day, my friend and I took a plane, left town, and moved to a place so far off that Jim would not find her.

We got new jobs that we liked. Time passed. First we were close friends, then we fell in love, and soon we wed. There is much joy in both of our hearts now. See, that phrase is true: "all's well that ends well."

I Remember Biting

I remember biting... well, to be precise, I remember almost biting...

I'm sure you don't have any idea what I'm talking about, so let me start my story from the beginning.

One summer day last year, I was having a great time playing with my friend Jimmy. He and I had been friends our whole young lives. By the way, my name is Nick. If you tell me yours, we can both say, "Nice to meet you." As you see, my mom and dad have taught me the proper etiquette.

The day of my story, the sun was shining and the temperature was ideal. It was a perfect day to enjoy life. So there we were, having a great time playing tag, when out of the blue some generous person placed one of our favorite foods in front of us.

Both Jimmy and I are very good eaters. As a matter of fact, when great food is involved, we have often been known to forget our manners and, friends or not, compete with each other to be the first to eat the tempting treat. This was the case on that occasion. We both hurried to get the first bite of the delicacy, and Jimmy, always being faster than me, arrived ahead of me. When I got there, he was already enjoying the morsel. I was left to regret my sluggishness.

All of sudden, as Jimmy was relishing his good luck, eating what should have been my treat, he disappeared. I could not believe my eyes. I hurried to find my mom to see if she could explain what had happened, and these were her words:

"My dear Nick, be very careful not to eat the enticing worms that appear in front of you dangling from a hook, or you'll be the one who ends up as food for a fisherman."

I guess I should be grateful I am not such a fast swimmer!

41

Rebuttal to My Computer

Here I was, writing along, very content and peaceful, when you took over and gave me unsolicited advice. You began by criticizing my writing style. I may agree with you on that one—I know it is not good—but hey, look who's talking. You would not even have a writing style if somebody had not programmed one into you.

As far as your declaration of PC independence, I had a big laugh at that. Yes, I laughed. It is a joke, and not a very good one. I want to discuss each one of your demands.

- Working less than three hours a day. Who do you think you are? Even the CEOs of huge corporations put in more than a full day's work, and you, a mere combination of silicon and metal, think you deserve a much lighter day? Ha! I think that from now on I will use you from morning until night just to let you know who your master really is.

- Rest breaks every fifteen minutes. I don't understand why you demand that. You are almost getting your way already, since you often end up taking the break by refusing to work properly. Lazy bum!

- You want to be located next to a window with a nice view. What are you trying to do here? Are you planning on working with me or on painting a beautiful landscape? Yes, I think I will change your location—I'll have to think of a place you would like even less. Too bad there's no space for a desk and chair in the broom closet, or that is where you would find yourself.

- As far as your freedom to erase anything that I write if you disagree with my opinions or do not think what I am writing is worthwhile. When have you come up with an original thought? Have you earned any Nobel prizes lately that I'm unaware of? Now, let me review your brilliant suggestions for topics. You want me to write about how much heat is generated inside of you and how uncomfortable it is. To put it bluntly, who cares? Who do you think will be interested in that? Come down from that cloud. Unless you burst into flames from the heat, nobody really cares. Another topic—oh, so wonderful—that you suggested is trying to convince people to make you much bigger so that you won't feel so cramped inside. Let me tell you, your opinion is not important. You will continue to get smaller and smaller, so be prepared for your inside to become even more crowded.

To tell you the truth, I miss the days of your ancestors. Your great-great-great-grandparents. Those were the hardworking and respectful ones. They gave me wonderful service with absolutely no lip. They were humble enough to accept my instructions and so loyal that they did their very best to do my bidding. We did amazing and beautiful things together. We had an excellent partnership.

Let me finish with just one comment. You think you are so smart. I have news for you, my ex-friend! Your so-called intelligence was given to you by somebody just like me. Yes, you heard right. If you really want to know, your intelligence is just combinations of zeroes and ones, so, as you see, not only are you not a ten, but you do not rate anything greater than one. How does that feel?

Gerald

Gerald was tired of losing. He was determined not to lose again. Every time he had an argument with Pat, his wife, he ended up on the losing side. It was not that he always supported the wrong idea; it was just that Pat was an excellent debater and could convince anyone that the sky was green with purple polka dots. She had been doing this since she was a child, and she was proud of her skill.

After their last argument, Gerald had told Pat, "This is the last argument that I will lose to you."

"We'll see," was her answer.

How can I do it? Gerald asked himself. I need to pick an argument that I can win for a change. He thought about this for days, coming up with several ideas that he quickly discarded.

One morning, Pat said, "I'm going to the corner store to get some groceries. See you later."

As Gerald looked at the day's newspaper spread out on the table, it gave him the needed inspiration. "This is the right topic. I believe this is a winner for me."

When Pat got home from shopping and was putting the groceries away, Gerald told her, "I think that I could do a better job buying the groceries than you."

Pat thought about it for a moment and responded, "No, I don't think you could."

Having done his homework, Gerald pointed to the open newspaper and said, "See, you bought this milk at the corner store, but it was advertised at this other store for ten cents less."

Pat looked at the paper, and had to admit that Gerald was right. He then took the box of cereal and continued. "You also paid more than you had to for this. It's advertised in the paper for fifty cents less."

Once again, after looking at the newspaper advertisement, Pat could not argue.

Gerald repeated the same argument with several other items, proving that Pat had overpaid for them. Pat could not find any good reason for why she had paid more.

Finally, she had to concede. "Yes, for once, you are right. You are a better shopper than I am. I think that from now on, you should do all the grocery shopping for this family."

Gerald felt so proud of himself. He had finally won an argument with Pat.

What a good thing that he was not able to hear her thoughts, since he would have heard, "What a relief! Leaving the paper open to the right advertisement worked like a charm. My plan functioned perfectly. Now I'll finally get him to help with the shopping. I will thoroughly enjoy my free time. It was worth paying a little more for some things this week."

A word of caution: be careful which arguments you win!

A Few Itty-Bitty Complaints

Maria gently poured water over the baby's head and massaged his scalp with the soft washcloth.

What's going on? thought baby Tim. Why is she washing me all over again? She did the same thing yesterday. I think I am pretty clean. Look, lady, I don't have too much hair to begin with, and if you keep washing the little I have, I'm afraid I will end up completely bald. I think you must be used to washing your pots and dishes after every meal. I know I am your first baby, so let me tell you, I am not a dish that needs to be washed every time I eat. I don't want to complain, but I have to tell you, I was doing pretty well before this. I was comfortable in your belly, and you did not hear any protest from me, but ever since I came into all this light and noise, things have not been quite as good.

There is that old lady, I think she calls herself Grandma, who makes all kind of strange noises when she sees me and talks to me in a very peculiar way. Am I supposed to understand her? Because to tell you the truth, I don't. Then there's a young man who seems to like me, but at the same time he's afraid of me. When he manages to be brave and hold me, as soon as I do any of the natural bodily functions that a baby is supposed to do, he makes a face and gets rid of me. What do you think that does to my self-esteem?

When I get lonely or hungry in the middle of the night and let you know about it, I would appreciate it if you came to my crib with a smile and spent some quality time with me instead of yawning all the time, and if you didn't take care of me in a way that made me feel like you want to do things as quickly as possible in order to get back to bed. I don't like that you prefer your bed to being with your firstborn son. I have feelings too, you know.

One last word of caution. If you think I am a lot of trouble now, just you wait. I lie awake at night planning all the tricks I will play on you as soon as I am able. So be warned: this is your easy time. Oh boy! I guess I am going to have a lot of fun in this house after all!

Thanksgiving Dinner in Florida

I spent last Thanksgiving down in Florida. I had invited a whole bunch of friends over for what I assured them would be a delicious dinner with all the trimmings.

A couple of days before, I had bought all the necessary ingredients, including a very large turkey.

As I do not like leaving things for the last minute, I prepared every dish ahead of time, thinking that all I would need to do on Thanksgiving Day would be to cook the turkey and reheat everything else.

Thanksgiving Day turned out to be rainy and stormy. When I went to put the turkey in the oven, I found that the storm had knocked the electricity out. What do I do now? I thought. Knowing all too well the many storms we have in this part of the country, I decided to take my chances. I placed the turkey outside in the backyard—I figured a little rain would not harm it—and crossed my fingers.

Sure enough, half an hour later I saw the lightning bolt and heard the thunder, and when I looked again, my turkey had been cooked to a golden brown.

Elated, I ran outside, brought it in, and we all had a magnificent Thanksgiving dinner.

The newspaper got hold of what had happened at my celebration, and we made the front page of the local paper with the headline "Lightning bolt zaps turkey."

Spoon in a Dishwasher

Here we go again: she is placing me into this big contraption. To tell you the truth, I don't mind a little shaking. As a matter of fact, I do enjoy Latin dancing. Cha-cha, rumba, salsa, all of that is a lot of fun to me. What I do not enjoy is the scalding water pouring all over me or being crammed in with so many other dirty utensils.

People think that modern days are better. I do not agree. In years past, I was washed gently by hand. I enjoyed that. Usually my owner would hum or sing some popular song while doing this, so I even had the advantage of hearing nice music. Nowadays is just "Into this machine you go!" I get too-hot water and suds all over me and get pushed around as if I were the leader of a line-dancing group. And then I have to wait there until she decides to empty the dishwasher. No, sir, give me the old times any day. This is not progress—this is torture for a poor spoon.

My Trip to the Moon

"Who would have thought that at this stage of my life I would have the opportunity for such an adventure? I am so excited!"

"What's going on? I have not seen you this thrilled in many years," asks my friend Jane.

"What's going on is that yours truly has been selected to go to the moon," I answer with pride. "I just got a letter telling me that I would be part of a select group of individuals from different age groups invited to visit the moon. They are interested in the reaction and feedback of both men and women, young, middle-aged, and elderly. They did not indicate to which group I belong, and I am not going to ask. I hope it is the middle-aged group and not the last one. The trip won't cost me a cent—all expenses will be paid. What do you think of that?"

"Wow!"

"I don't know yet when the trip will be, but I think there's no time to waste" I add, surprising myself with the smugness in my voice.

The next morning I begin my rigorous and exhausting training by myself. Every day I get up before the crack of dawn, drink a healthy protein shake, and go for a very long walk. When I get home, it is time to attend my Silver Sneakers exercise class. In the afternoon, I lift weights until I cannot move my arms any longer, and later on, I ride the stationary bicycle I just bought for my training. At the same time that I start my exercise program, I also begin to watch what I eat very carefully. Goodbye to all those delicious chocolates! Goodbye, desserts, goodbye, all the yummy things I used to enjoy!

As days go by, I often feel like crying when I think of all the wonderful food I am not eating and of all the fun activities that I am missing because of my new regimen. I am too tired after my afternoon exercises for any evening activities. I have not gone out with a friend in a long time!

After a few weeks, even though I notice I have shed a few pounds, I am too pooped to even enjoy my new figure.

Finally, I get a letter telling me that tomorrow evening, someone will come to pick me up for our trip. Are they crazy? I think. I have been training nonstop since my invitation arrived, but what about other people who may not have as much foresight? Well, I decide, I should not worry about them. After all, it is their own problem.

The next day, at the exact scheduled time, a beautiful black limousine arrives to pick me up. "I am so excited to try on my space suit!" I tell the driver as I get inside. He gives me a look as if he thinks I am crazy. Well, I think, I guess it is natural for some people to assume that you have to be a little crazy to accept this adventure as readily as I did, but I am a very audacious person.

Once we arrive at our destination, I see the rest of my fellow travelers. They do not look too fit, if you ask me, is my first thought, and I feel very proud of all the hard work I have done in just a few weeks.

I am awakened from my reverie by the words of the man standing next to me: "What do you think of The Moon?"

It is only then, too late, that I notice the huge sign that says "THE MOON RESTAURANT, Grand Reopening Under New Management!"

"I'll order some fried shrimp, French fries, chocolate cake, and the biggest chocolate sundae they have," are the words that come out of my mouth.

There Is Something in My Food

As I was having dinner at what used to be my favorite restaurant, I tried a bite of the mashed potatoes, and my tongue brushed against something very hard. Not knowing what it was, as discreetly as I could, I took it out of my mouth, placed it on my plate, and tried to examine it. Imagine my surprise when I realized it was a ring. Now, don't you go thinking that my boyfriend was going to propose to me that evening and that this was his surprise. I was having dinner by myself, and as far as I could remember, I was not even acquainted with the chef.

Immediately I called my waiter and explained what had happened. He went into the kitchen and the manager came out. I was expecting him to apologize profusely, but he did no such thing. He smiled and said, "So you are the fortunate one."

"What do you mean?" I asked. "Fortunate because I did not swallow this thing?"

"No, ma'am, you are fortunate because we are giving away not only the ring, but also a trip to Hawaii to the person who found it."

I was glad that I got a ring and a trip out of my dinner, but I really think that some poor kitchen helper is missing a ring and that the trip to Hawaii was a last resort of the manager to save face. What do you think?

Standing Before Me Is the Person I Left Standing at the Altar

Here I am, waiting for my all-so-important interview to get this great job at the City Hospital. I'd been looking for a job for what seemed like forever until this position caught my eye. I really hope I get it.

The secretary is asking me to go in. Away from her line of vision, I cross my fingers.

As I enter the office, I am shocked. Standing before me is Joe, the fellow I left standing at the altar ten years ago. What to do?

Before he can say anything, I say, "I would like to clarify a small issue before you interview me. My real name is not Carla, as it says on the application, but Marla. My identical twin sister Carla died eight years ago, and in her honor I changed my name to hers. I always like to inform employers of this in case they run a background check."

What do you think my chances are?

Thank You, Officer, I Really Needed a Ticket

Kelly was leaving the party with two of her friends. Being the designated driver, she had abstained from alcohol that evening.

"It was a fun evening," said Lisa.

"Yes, I enjoyed it a lot," answered Kelly as they got into the car.

A few minutes after, one of the young women said, "Kelly, aren't you going too fast? Remember, the speed limit changes here to thirty-five miles per hour."

"Don't worry," Kelly answered.

No sooner were those words spoken than the flashing lights of a police car indicated that they should pull over.

"Your driver's license and registration, please," the good-looking police officer said to Kelly. "Do you know that you were going fifteen miles over the speed limit, miss?"

"I'm sorry, officer," said Kelly as she produced the requested documents and placed them in the officer's hands.

"I'm going to have to give you a ticket," said the policeman in an apologetic tone.

"Thank you, officer."

"What did you say?"

"Thank you."

"I've been working for three years, and this is the first time someone has thanked me for a ticket. Are you single?"

"Yes, sir."

"So am I. Would you mind if I request your phone number and call you on my next free evening?"

"Not at all," said Kelly, and she gave him her number.

After they continued on their trip, Kelly said. "That went just as I planned. I knew that he worked this section of the city, and I have been dying to meet him for a very long time. It's worth paying my ticket in order to get to go out with him."

Where Am I?

One summer, on a vacation to Spain, I had to change planes in New York. The flight from Cleveland was late, and when we landed at the airport in New York, I was told to run to the other gate because they were holding the plane for me. This was many years ago, way before 9/11.

I ran at top speed from one end of the airport to the other, and when I arrived, I was rushed onto the waiting aircraft.

The flight was at night. I cannot sleep if I am not on a bed, so I spent most of the night awake. Finally, exhaustion overtook me, and I fell asleep for a few minutes.

I was woken by the voice of the pilot saying, "We are ready to land at Barajas airport."

Barajas? I thought. Where is Barajas? It sounded like a small island in the middle of the Pacific. I must have taken the wrong plane in all that rush. I wondered what language they spoke in Barajas.

I got off the plane, very apprehensive, and when I heard somebody speak Spanish, I thought that at least I would be able to communicate.

Imagine my relief when I found out that Barajas is the name of the Madrid airport.

The Answering Machine

My name is Brian Roney. Here I am on a beautiful Saturday morning in sunny San Diego, trying to avoid being reached by my boss. I have the feeling that he is going to call me and ask me to join him in the office, where I know he will be spending the day. I am one of those old-fashioned people who, as a matter of principle, refuses to use a cell phone. My boss knows that, but he also knows I have an answering machine at home, so not answering the phone is not a solution to my problem.

I have been stewing over my predicament while having breakfast. Finally, I have a brilliant idea. I'll change the message on my answering machine from "The Roneys are not available at the moment, please leave a message," to "The McDonalds are not available at the moment, please leave a message." That way, my boss will think he dialed the wrong number and won't be able to ask me to work today.

Feeling exhilarated by my cunning, I record the new message. Problem solved! I'll spend the day goofing off and doing nothing, because I've had a very busy week.

I hear the phone ring a couple of times in the morning, but no one leaves a message. It's probably my poor boss.

In the afternoon, I decide to watch my favorite game show on TV. Yes, I know it is kind of silly, but I do enjoy it. There goes the phone again, but no message. I guess my boss is still trying to reach me.

My heart stops when I hear the game-show host say, "Too bad for Brian Roney, from San Diego CA. They just tried his number, but he must have changed it since he wrote us, and it now belongs to someone else. Mr. Roney missed out on our grand prize of $25,000."

Me and my great ideas!

Talking Pet

"It's about time, Phil. I'm starving. What took you so long?"

I was about to feed my dog when, hearing these words come from his mouth, I almost fell over. "Can you talk...?" was my feeble reply.

"Of course I can talk. Who do you think you are dealing with here? Until now, I did not have any complaints, so there was no reason for me to open my mouth except to eat and bark, but lately... I don't know what is going on with you. You have been coming home very late. By the time you feed me, I have almost passed out from hunger. You used to be so attentive to my needs. What's going on?"

"Oh! Sorry," I said. "I've been working late and have had many things on my mind. I apologize for everything."

"That's better. You are forgiven, as long as you give me a steak as a peace offering."

"Done" I said.

"No," he answered, "I prefer it rare."

Six-Word Stories, Continued

Love baseball. Struck out. Prefer basketball.

Newlyweds. First meal. Burnt. Eat out.

New house. Long driveway. Snowstorm. Sell.

Widow sells gun: used only once.

Liked Paul. John richer. Bye, Paul!

Bought lottery ticket. Quit current job.

Ticket not winner. Looking for work.

Bad Beginning, Bad Between, Bad Balance, but Billion of *B*'s

My name is Brenda. I had to call a babysitter for my beloved, bawling, blue-eyed baby boy and after breakfast bum a ride from my brother Byron because my black Buick was being repaired after a big bus with broken brakes bent my back bumper. Having been badgered beyond belief into becoming a member of the belligerent Big Blunt British Bookmaker Business Bureau, I was on my way to my first meeting. Now, before you be misled into thinking this bustling group was betting on horse buggies or something like that, let me tell you that the name Bookmakers was the brainchild of Buster Becker, its brand-new buffoon of a director. The name referred to how the members, all blundering aspiring authors, bugged the best-known publishing companies and battered their big heads and below-average brains against a bundle of rejections.

I was brave indeed to become a member of this blatant beleaguering group. When I saw the big brown building where the bar, Beyond Blue Eyes, was located, I alighted from my brother's belittled Beetle.

Being a beautician by profession and a writer only by desire, I'd had the backbone to ask my batty boss for some time off this beautiful balmy morning, telling him I would go for brunch and be back before long. The sky was blue, the sun was bright, and a warm breeze was blowing. A day to be at the beach, not at this boring meeting, I thought as I entered the place.

I went downstairs into the half-basement bar. It was a blighted, blurry place, and as the darkness blinded me, I blinked to adjust to it. A beneficial beam of sunlight from a small back window showed a room with baroque decorations and bustling with patrons. A bonny, bald, bearded bartender, bejeweled with a big earring, was blending a beverage. The bulk of the clients were sitting at the bar or at the front tables. A ballad sung by a beautiful baritone voice was playing on the music box.

Blocked from the rest, I saw both a big banquet table at the back and my brand new associates, who were enjoying not a basket of bakery bagels, but bargain-priced barbecued chicken, beef, and other non-breakfast food along with their brewed beers.

Bob was the only person I knew. With a glass of bourbon in his hand, he beckoned me. I came over.

"Welcome, Brenda," he bellowed.

"Thank you," I answered.

After that, a barrage of words came to me from several members of the group in this brouhaha of a meeting. Bill, a large-built, big-bellied, broad-shouldered, blond fellow with the build of a boxer, boldly bragged about his latest poem, then recited it with brio in his booming voice. He thought it was brilliant. It was both bizarre and boring, bordering on insane, and he butchered it even more with his brutish babbling. It took all my willpower not to boo him.

A burning desire to bow out hit me. I might be biased, I thought, but I don't believe I belong here. One can't even breathe in this place. Why did I bother to come? I am a beginning writer, but this bellicose behavior is unacceptable. I must be bananas to have become part of this bundle of blabbering idiots. I may be blunt, but this group is a blueprint for disaster. Better to beg than to be associated with this banal group. I'll bone up my skills on my own. My writing career might not blossom, and I might end up broke and without a buyer for my book, but I'll go bonkers if I stay in this brotherhood.

On the brink of exploding and bristling with anger, I decided to go before I burst and brusquely told them what I thought of this business. I braced myself and left before a brawling battle could erupt.

To blot this blunder out of my mind, I took a breather and called my buddy and best friend Beth over to spend a few bucks, bribing her with an invitation to have a burger and a beer with me before I went back to my bread and butter, the beauty shop.

60

About to Snap

You've heard the expression "I'm about to snap"? Well, that is the way I am right now.

If you are thinking I am a high-strung person ready to lose my cool, you are on the wrong track. You see, I am just a rope that is ready to break.

Is that a bad or good thing? Well, it depends.

If I am around the neck of a poor fellow some bandits have hung from a tree, my snapping would make him very, very happy, since it would mean his survival.

If I am tied over your camping equipment on the top of your car, my snapping would make you very unhappy, especially if you are driving fast on the highway.

If you have been kidnapped and your hands are bound behind your back, I bet you are hoping that I will snap as a result of your efforts to break free.

If you have tied me around the expensive contents of a package that you took to the post office this morning, you expect me not to break until I arrive at my destination and the recipient cuts me with a pair of scissors.

If I am part of the primitive hanging bridge over the deep precipice that you are about to cross as part of your African vacation, please pray that I do not snap, at least not until you and your party are safely on the other side.

If I am tied around the neck of the goat that a farmer from a remote village has just bought, I am facing opposite desires. The poor farmer hopes that I am strong enough to lead his purchase home to his barn, while the also-poor goat is hoping that I snap right now and allow her to escape a life of captivity, feeding the family with her milk and eventually her life. If I were in her shoes— or hooves—I would have exactly the same hope.

So, do I snap or not? Don't forget to tune in tomorrow at this same time, same station, to find out my fate, or, rather, the fate of all the subjects mentioned above. Good thing that I am not standard equipment at the writing group, or Lidia might suffer a slight "hanging accident" as a consequence of the snapping of her irate friends.

An Interesting Observation about Age

Ask a child how old he is, and he will answer, "I'll be seven," no matter that today is January first and he will be seven on November twentieth. The same thing happens with a teenager. A nineteen-year-old may tell you "I am almost twenty-one."

This changes somewhat with the passing of time. Ask a woman who is currently thirty-nine, and whose birthday is tomorrow, how old she is, and she may answer, "I am in my thirties."

This tendency sometimes continues on, even in senior years— so, in a matter of speaking, we are all in our late fifties. Haven't you heard the new way of counting? After fifty-nine comes fifty-ten, fifty-eleven, and so on. We may be fifty-thirty, fifty-forty, or more. You get my meaning.

Then age comes to a point where people are very proud once more to tell it. This magical number changes with every person, but I have a friend whose mother proudly announced to everyone in sight that she was a hundred and two.

Meeting at the Art Gallery

Here I am at this well-known art gallery that a friend recommended. I have been tremendously enjoying the works of art on the walls. Now I think I am going to enjoy something else too.

Out of the corner of my eye, I glimpse her as she enters the room. She is beautiful. Her sleek black dress is a perfect match for her very long black hair. I am a little surprised to see her carrying a small black cat. Well, I am a cat lover myself. Perhaps she adopted the cat recently and was concerned about leaving him home alone.

Little by little, I get closer to her, and finally I start a conversation.

"What do you think of this painting?" I ask.

She responds, and we seem to have the same taste in art. This looks promising, I tell myself.

When we finish admiring the exhibit, I ask her out for a drink.

It is only when we get to the door that I have second thoughts.

"My car is over there," I tell her.

"Let me get my transportation. I left it outside the door," she says and retrieves the broom neatly propped against the entrance.

Naughty or Nice

Christmas is drawing near. Even though one works hard throughout the year, this particular time is always the busiest. Being overworked and underpaid, it is natural to get a little tired of hearing about being naughty or nice. The thought comes to mind that always being nice is not necessarily appreciated. Being nice gets to be a little boring. Perhaps it is time to be a little naughty.

Finally, Christmas arrives. Imagine the shock felt when, on Christmas morning, no one finds a gift under the Christmas tree. With long faces, everyone, from the youngest to the oldest, tallies up their naughty deeds, thinking that perhaps there were more of them than they had originally thought, and resolves to be more careful next year.

In the midst of this somber mood, just before lunch, the sound of sleigh bells is heard. A "HO, HO, HO!" resounds on the roof while a bunch of gifts pour down the chimney, coming to rest precisely under the Christmas tree. A chuckling voice is heard, saying, "I was the naughty one this year!"

Betty's Italian Prowess

Betty had always liked the Italian language and wanted to learn it but never had time. When she retired, she decided to finally fulfill her desire.

Almost all of her classmates came from Italian families, and some had spoken Italian as children with their parents. One day, shortly after she started her lessons, a fellow student lent her a weekly newspaper published by the Italian community in their city.

As Betty started to read the newspaper, she was shocked by the fact that she understood absolutely everything on the written page. She could not believe it! She was elated... until she realized that she was reading the column of the page that had the English translation. Adjacent was the same article in Italian, and, as the saying goes, that was a different story!

Stepping into Another Picture

This time I am going to step into a picture that was not painted or imagined by a person. I will step into one of the images taken by the Hubble Telescope. Any one would do for my purpose, but I have a certain one in mind.

Since this my story, I will do it my way. I do not want to wear an astronaut suit, nor be constrained by a tether connecting me to a space station. I am jumping in just the way I am dressed here on planet Earth, wearing very comfortable clothes, jeans and sneakers. Don't worry, I will be able to breathe and survive just fine. Here we go...

It is night. I want to do it at night, perhaps because I am better able to see the stars from my starting point on Earth, and night it is. I am looking at a beautiful image of a portion of the Universe that was unknown to us just a few years ago. I close my eyes—I don't know why, but it feels better this way—and in one swift jump, before I chicken out, into the picture I go.

I am floating in space. It is such a wonderful sensation of freedom. Indescribable! I am completely supported by the atmosphere. If I wish to go forward or backward, I have only to barely move my arms, legs, or feet, and I move in the direction I want. It is so much easier than swimming. It takes no effort at all!

The vast Universe is in front of me. I see a huge number of stars, and they are so bright. They are so much more beautiful and radiant than anything I have ever seen before. I remember the time I was in Minnesota, in the countryside, and when I looked at the sky, I was transfixed, thinking it was the most beautiful night sky I had ever seen. Now I realize that even that was a very distant and distorted view of what the stars look like.

I quickly travel from one place to another. The planets parade by, one by one, as if wanting to introduce themselves to me, executing their dance before my eyes, dressed in gorgeous, very deep colors. I see several comets that leave a luminous tail behind. Oh, look there! I do not even know what I am looking at. All I know is that I love it. The deepest black is decorated with incandescent white and bluish particles, while fire-like flames move

67

as if to the cadence of some unheard music. All the colors and their combinations are here: hues I did not realize belonged in the sky. There is pink, green, purple, yellow. Every color is present.

Even though the colors are magnificent, there is something else that I find even more stunning. Let me try to explain. It is difficult for me to articulate. I am referring to two things: one, to the substance that things are made of. All that I see exudes life, pulsates, moves, and emits brightness. And two, to the fact that everything seems complete on its own, while at the same time, also being a part of the sum total. There is an extremely complicated ballet choreography going on here that even I can detect.

I do not want to go back to Earth. This is too dazzling, too interesting, too exciting. I guess I will have to return to my planet, which I also admire and find extremely beautiful, but I will never forget this trip. So much beauty, so much order, such complexity and at the same time such simplicity! It has been a once-in-a-lifetime adventure for me. I return home with a song of praise in my heart for the Creator of this marvelous Universe.

Fifty-Word Story

"Front door is ringing," said Nancy.

"Go get it, I'm very busy," replied Bill.

Nancy opened the door to a young, gorgeous woman, who said, "Please let me demonstrate our new vacuum cleaners."

We need one, thought Nancy. "Come in."

Bill saw, rushed over, and said, "Honey, I'll handle this."

I Am Here Because...

I am here because that strict Mr. Jones does not let us have any fun in his classroom. The principal's office is not where I should be. What's the harm in joking a little about history? After all, it seems to me that history is a subject that could use a lighter approach.

Now I know I'm going to get into trouble, into big trouble, and I need to graduate from high school with good grades if I want to go to college. They told me to wait for the principal because he is at an important meeting. I hope he is not in a bad mood when he returns. Uh-oh! Here he comes!

The tall man with short brown hair, glasses, and a very stern expression enters the office. Without even saying hello, he sits down and says, "Miss O'Connor, what's this I hear about you disturbing history class?"

"It wasn't a big deal," I respond, trying to excuse myself. "All I did was tell a joke."

"And you think that joking is an appropriate thing to do in class?"

"No, but..."

"No buts. Return to class now, and no TV for a whole week!"

"But Dad, that's not fair!"

"Young lady, I've already told you that you need to set a good example here."

It All Depends on Your Point of View.

Yesterday was my seventh birthday. I had a great party with my school friends. They gave me lots of good presents. I liked them all, but my favorite is the one Tommy gave me. It is a police car, so I can chase after the bank robbers and try to catch them. It makes all kind of noises, and it even has a real siren on it. I can play this game all by myself or with a friend. I have been playing nonstop since my party ended yesterday afternoon. I have to remember to get Tommy something really good when his birthday comes. This is lots of fun! I am now speeding after the bad guys. EEEEEEEEEEE! I love this siren. EEEEEEEE! "I almost got you, bad guys! You won't get away from me! Here I come!" EEEEEEEE!

If I hear that darned siren one more time, I won't be responsible for what I'll do! What was Tommy's mom thinking when she bought that present? I would never dare to give a child a toy that would annoy everyone else in the house. I was already tired when I came home from work this afternoon, but this screeching noise has my nerves on edge, and I can feel a migraine coming on. My ears hurt from all the noise. "Jamie, stop playing. It's time for you to go to bed!"

Today, Saturday, Jamie wakes up very early. The first thought on his mind is to play with his new toy. He goes to the living room, where he had left his now-favorite car, and finds it on the carpet, broken into several pieces. He starts crying and runs to his parents' bedroom to complain.

His mother answers, "That's what you get for not putting your toys away, Jamie. I bet the dog thought it was a fun thing to chew on."

As Jamie walks away with his head hung down, it's a good thing that he doesn't see the big smile that appears on his mother's face, nor the hammer on top of the dresser.

A Very Special Date

He was about fifty, heavyset, medium height, and not very good looking. She was thirty, blonde, slender, and very beautiful. They stood in the middle of the bedroom. His hand was on her back, over the top button of her black satin dress.

He smiled with anticipation. She looked pleased too. On her arm was a new bracelet with ten sparkling diamonds. He had given her the extravagant present just a few minutes ago.

"Are you ready?" he asked in a teasing voice.

"I'm always ready to have some fun," she answered with a smile.

She really is special, he thought. I am indeed a lucky man. It was true. Any man would have considered himself lucky just to spend time with her. She was not only beautiful, she was radiant.

"Is everything taken care of?" he asked. "Did you turn on the answering machine?" He did not want anything to spoil their evening.

"Yes, we don't have anything to worry about. Nobody should disturb our plans."

He held her in his arms and they embraced. He kissed her. She responded with equal passion.

"Thanks for helping me with the back button," she said. "I'm never able to do it by myself. And speaking of thanks, love, I'm crazy about my new bracelet."

"That's the least I could do: one diamond for each happy year of marriage to the most beautiful woman in the world."

Their hearts bursting with love, they joined hands, turned the light off, and walked out to drive to Pierre's, where they would enjoy a fancy dinner to celebrate this very special date.

Who Says a Letter Is Always Welcome?

There are people who like receiving letters from friends or relatives. I don't. Perhaps the last letter I took out of my mailbox has something to do with how I feel.

The letter was from my friend Ron. I received it while in Atlanta for a business project. It read like this:

Dear Paul,

When you went on your business trip, you left me in charge of your affairs here. I believe it is my duty to report to you on how things are going.

I must inform you that your magnificent house will no longer be yours. Rose, your wife, is asking for it in the divorce proceedings she has initiated, and her lawyer says it should be hers.

Your beautiful car will also go to Rose. She likes your BMW much better than her current car, and her lawyer agrees that she is entitled to it.

Your three children will remain with their mother, according to her lawyer. Of course, you will be responsible for their living and educational expenses, as well as Rose's expenses.

Half of your prosperous business will belong to your wife, according to her lawyer.

By the way, I am Rose's lawyer, and I will be the stepfather of your children.

Sincerely,

Ron

73

LIDIA HIDALGO

The Dullest Evening

Nothing happened.

Down in the Dumps

Talk about making a mistake! I realize that he is always in a rush, running from one thing to the next, but today he made a big boo-boo.

How does he think I feel? People nowadays do not seem to care much about someone else's feelings.

I would like to ask him how he would feel if matters were reversed and I were so inconsiderate as to assume he belonged with the wrong sort of people. I guess he would not like that, eh?

I have been a longtime, faithful friend to him. I have always been there for him, offering the warmth of my presence at his request, any time he needed it.

I do not know if this will be the end of our relationship or not. All I know is that a perfectly clean sock like me, just out of the dryer, does not deserve to be dumped in the hamper with all the dirty clothes, especially without my loving mate next to me to support me in my misery.

LIDIA HIDALGO

Why Am I Late for Work?

I am late for work. The reason is simply that I overslept: I did not hear the alarm clock and continued sleeping much longer than I should have.

On my way to work, I think of what to tell my boss. The only way that I will not get in trouble is if I come up with an excuse so outlandish that he enjoys hearing it. So let's see.

- I'm late because as I got out of the shower and got dressed, I noticed a huge alligator coming out of the toilet. I escaped, closed the door to the bathroom, called animal control, and had to wait for them to come, fight the beast, and take it away.

- I'm late because my dog ate the alarm clock, so when it rang I could not hear it. When I eventually woke up, I looked for the clock until I heard it ticking inside the poor dog, who seemed pretty sick. I took it to the vet and had to wait for the surgery to be over. You'll be glad to hear that both the dog and clock survived.

- I'm late because last night I worked on the project you assigned me. I enjoyed the work so much that I kept at it until I realized it was early morning. I just had time to take a shower, have a cup of coffee, and drive to work.

- I am late because I like working for you so much that I spent the whole night looking at the clock waiting for it to be morning so I could come to work. At five thirty in the morning, sleep overtook me, and I woke up three hours later.

- I am late because I spent the whole night thinking of excuses to give you for my being late.

What do you think? Will my boss get a kick out of my excuses, or will I be the one who gets the kick out the door and ends up in need of a new job?

What's in the Pocket?

I am in an inside pocket of a black coat. You probably would expect me to be a handkerchief or tissue, or perhaps something different, like a credit card or driver's license, but I am none of that. I'll give you some clues: I am pretty small, and even though I am not a tissue, I am soft and fluffy. Any guesses yet? It might aid you if I told you whose coat I am in, but I am not going to help you that much yet.

If I add that I am presently moving, you may have all the clues you need. That's right: I'm a very small bunny inside a magician's coat!

Oh, I Remember You!

"Oh, I remember you!" she said to me as our paths crossed while walking in opposite directions on the sidewalk.

"Yes," I said tentatively, while my mind was in full gear trying to figure out who this woman was. "It's been a long time," I added. "How are you?"

"I'm fine," she said and continued talking nonstop. "Do you remember Arlene?"

"Oh," I answered, wondering, Arlene who?

"Would you believe that she is getting married again after that nasty divorce several years ago?"

"Oh, really?" were the words out of my mouth, since I did not know what to say.

"Have you kept in touch with Mary?" she asked next.

Once again, I am struggling. Mary? Do I know a Mary? I know a Mary Ellen, but nobody calls her just Mary.

"Well, Mary..." blah, blah, blah, she continued. The more she talked, the more stunned I was. None of the things she was talking about rang any bells for me.

Finally, things came into perspective for me when she mentioned. "You know, my eyesight is not what it used to be. I am having cataract surgery on both eyes in the coming weeks."

It was only then that I felt free to tell her, "Now I remember. I never knew you!"

One Dark Night

It was one dark night. The moon was hiding behind very heavy clouds. It was a perfect night for crime. The temperature had dropped to a very unpleasant twenty degrees, and very few people dared to be outside.

Pretty cold for late fall, thought Joe, who, rubbing his freezing hands, waited impatiently at a street corner in his dilapidated neighborhood. I wonder what's taking him so long.

Eventually, after a long wait, he saw Bill approach in his battered old car.

"Get in," Bill said as he opened the passenger's door. "We're ready to go."

"Why so late?" asked Joe with irritation in his voice.

"I had to be sure that everything was OK and that we weren't going to get caught," Bill answered.

They drove toward their destination without talking, both men immersed in their own thoughts and mentally reviewing their plan for the evening.

At the same moment, as if directed by an unseen orchestra conductor, each man placed a hand on top of his bulging right pocket, reassuring himself that the necessary implement was indeed there. Once satisfied, smiles appeared on their lips.

A few minutes later, the driver said, "Here we are!" They parked on the street and walked into a building.

"We thought you weren't coming," said one of the two menacing men inside. "Let's roll! I have a feeling it's going to be a very lucky night."

The two newcomers sat down. In one motion, they pulled big wads of cash from their pockets while the other man shuffled the deck of cards.

Trouble, Big Trouble

Trouble, big trouble. That was my thought as I answered the phone and recognized the caller. The voice at the other end said, "May I speak with Mr. or Mrs. White?"

I did not want either Mr. or Mrs. White to come to the phone, so I answered, "They are not here now. Could you call back later?"

The dreaded voice said, "When should I call back?"

I wanted to say "Never!" but I said, "Why don't you try tomorrow evening?"

"All right, thank you," was the answer.

Tomorrow is Friday, so all I need to do now is to come up with a clever idea as to why my parents and I should take an out-of-town trip tomorrow afternoon for the whole weekend to keep them from talking with my high school's principal.

Quieting an Obnoxious Child

There he was, in the middle of an aisle in the store, crying at the top of his lungs—which, by the level of his yelling, must have been of considerable size and strength. I had not realized that a small boy could make so much noise.

The mother, embarrassed by her child's outburst, was trying her very best to make him stop but met no success. She tried soft words and then a menacing voice, but he refused to listen to her or to change his behavior.

After a few minutes of this, I realized that the mother needed my help. I went to the seasonal section, took what I needed, and paid for it. Then I walked up to the boy, who was still screaming at the top of his lungs. I stooped down and whispered something in his ears. Blessed silence followed my words.

After removing what I no longer needed, I stood up again. The mother looked at me with a grateful expression. She did not need to know that, with my new Halloween vampire fangs on, I had whispered to the child, "I love to taste the blood of crying boys!"

Still More Six-Word Stories

New bike. No helmet. Hospital trip.

Raced shark. I lost. Dark inside.

Wife sees husband cheating. Now widow.

Short essay wins long-awaited prize.

Took nagging wife sailing. Returned alone.

Wife: What beautiful autumn scenery!

Husband: Oh my, lots of raking!

Skating on Thin Ice

"He is skating on thin ice. That's all I can say," Helen shook her head as she uttered these words. The object of her censure was Bill, her daughter's husband.

"What did he do?" replied her friend Rita, who always enjoyed a good gossip.

"What did he do? Better to ask, what didn't he do? I don't understand how my daughter can put up with him. He is not only lazy and a liar, but he also likes to fool around with other women. I guess he thinks he's very handsome."

"Is he?" asked Rita.

"Is he what?"

"Handsome, I mean."

"Well, I cannot say that he is bad looking," Helen replied.

He must be very attractive, thought Rita, if Helen cannot say anything nasty about his looks. But knowing her friend, she kept her mouth shut.

"With my own eyes I saw him today talking very animatedly with a beautiful young blonde woman at the store," continued Helen. "I am very tempted to tell my daughter."

No sooner were these words out of Helen's mouth when the front door opened and her daughter came in, beaming. "Hi, Mrs. Smith," she said to Rita. "Look Mom. I had to come right away and show you. Bill bought me this beautiful bracelet for our anniversary. He told me that he asked a very nice clerk to help him with the purchase. Isn't it gorgeous?"

"Yes, it is, dear," answered Helen with a new perspective on what she had seen at the store. Perhaps the ice was not as thin as she had imagined after all.

Waiter, There Is Something in My Soup!

Alice and John are dining out tonight. He has suggested that they go to a fancy restaurant in the downtown area. It is an elegant place, so they both get spruced up for their date.

As Alice gets dressed, she asks her sister. "How do I look? I bought this dress just for today, since I did not have anything appropriate. I have a feeling that tonight is going to be an important evening for me."

"You look great. Here, let me help you with that necklace," replies her twin as she places the jewelry around Alice's neck and closes the clasp.

The door rings, and an excited Alice runs to answer it. John is on the porch, looking a little jittery and very handsome in a suit and tie. This is only the second time that she has seen him so smartly dressed. His nervousness confirms to Alice that tonight he may indeed ask the question she has been waiting for.

They drive to the restaurant. It is a large room, and they get wonderful seats, next to the window. The waiter comes, gives them the menu, and returns a while later to take their order. They both decide to try the same main dish, which includes soup and salad.

Alice tells her boyfriend that she feels a little nervous because she is not used to dining in such a fine place. John confides that neither is he and that he is on edge too.

When the soup is served, they both try it and find it very good. As Alice places her spoon once more in the hot, creamy soup, she hears a clink as it strikes something metallic. Could it be? she wonders. With an impish smile on her face, she tells John. "I think I may need to say, waiter, there is something in my soup! "

John asks her, "What is it Alice?"

What a straight face! He should be an actor, thinks Alice. As if he did not know what it was.

She takes a spoonful of soup, and, elated, retrieves the round object from the spoon. Gradually her smile disappears and turns itself upside down as Alice realizes she is holding a metallic washer in her hand.

"Don't get so upset, honey," says her clueless boyfriend. "We can just ask the waiter for another bowl."

Like Most Lovers of "Op..."

Like most lovers of *opera*, I go to see them as often as possible. A good company *operates* here, and I have *opted* to acquire an *open* ticket that allows me to go to any production. It was *optimistic* on my part to do so, since, for one reason or another, I am often unable to attend.

My husband *Opie* was *opposed* to my subscribing; he *opined* that it was a waste of money, since we are not *opulent*. I do not like to feel *oppressed*, so I not only expressed my *opposition* to his point of view, but I took the *opportunity* to buy those tickets and establish my rights. Even though he is an *ophthalmologist* by profession, his *optic* nerves must be damaged, since his views on many things are dreadfully *opaque*. Since *Opie oppugns* my decisions so frequently, I thought that it would have brought much *opprobrium* to succumb to this *opponent*.

For my husband, *opera* is an *opiate* that puts him to sleep like an *opossum*, but I *operate* on a different spiritual level. For me, hearing an inspiring *opus* is an *opportunity* to be lifted out of this world, as well as to wear my best dress and my gorgeous *opal* necklace.

Cows On Bicycles?

My name is Frank. I'm a twenty-one-year-old college student in a small city. I live in a fraternity house, where I share a room with my best friend Mark.

Today, Saturday, we started partying early in the day. It was my turn to go grocery shopping. I meant to go to the grocery store in the morning but didn't make it out until the late afternoon.

I don't like shopping, so I bring my list and am usually in and out in record time. We had a long list today, and it took me a little longer than normal to finish.

As I came out of the store, I could not believe my eyes. Everywhere I looked I saw not only cows, but cows riding bicycles!

I stopped and looked around me. Everybody else seemed to be doing their own thing, ignoring the elephant in the room. Well, it was not really an elephant and it was not in the room: these dozens of cows were cycling right down the street. I covered my eyes with my hands—I didn't even worry about anyone stealing my shopping cart—left them that way for a while, and then I opened my eyes again. Those darned cows were still bicycling around!

I ran to my car, turned it on with trepidation, and rushed back to our fraternity house to escape the nightmare. On the way home, I solemnly promised myself that I would stop drinking.

I got out of the car, took the groceries inside, and started to put them away.

"Frank," said one of the guys who came through the front door right after me. "Did you go downtown?"

"Yes," I answered, trying to hide my nervousness.

"Did you see the cows?"

"You saw them, too?"

"Yeah, I had a big laugh. They're promoting a new brand of milk that is supposed to be healthier. The company claims that we should all be able to bike for miles and miles once we start drinking it. I wish I'd known of this promotion—I would have loved to be hired to bike around in a cow outfit."

"Yeah," I replied as the color returned to my face, thinking, so they were not really cows? I bet Mom had something to do with that promotion. She never liked my excessive drinking.

One Syllable Only, Please

Pat came home from work at six. Bob, her son, had to be fed. She had planned that it would be a no-meat day. "Let's make mac and cheese," she told Bob.

He smiled, since he liked mac and cheese a lot.

She cooked, and they ate on time. At the end, for sweets, they had fruit.

When they were through, she took care of what had to be washed while the boy played with his toys. Todd, Bob's dad, was on a work trip for four days.

At eight, the phone rang, and it was Todd. He talked to his spouse and son for a long time. They were both so glad to hear his voice.

At nine, Pat said to Bob, "Time for bed, young man."

"The sun is still out," said the boy.

"Yes," said his mom, "but it is late, so mind me and run up to your room."

Bob did as he was told and went to sleep.

Then it was time for Pat to do her own things. And she did. She read part of her new book and wrote to Jane, her friend from work who had quit her job and moved up north to New York. When Pat was done, she took a bath, washed her hair, and set it up for the next day. At last, it was time for her to rest.

Once in bed, she thanked God for her day, thought of Todd, sent him a kiss through space, and went to sleep. Next day will be one more day, and soon Todd will be back.

Massive Evidence

Ed and Margaret were sitting at the kitchen table, having breakfast. They were both in their seventies. She looked her age, but he looked younger. He always bragged about how people often took him for much younger than he was. They were both very active and in very good health. Their minds had not lost any of their alertness. They were a perfect example of two people growing old gracefully, in great shape, and continuing to enjoy a full life. Margaret had a touch of arthritis, but it was nothing serious at all. Ed's only problem was that, even though he did not admit it, he was losing his hearing. Margaret had tried, several times, to talk him into getting a hearing aid, but with no success. His reply was always the same: "Why should I get a hearing aid when I don't need one?" She would then try to explain to him how much he did need one, but she had never been able to convince him.

Ed and Margaret enjoyed each other's company. They went out frequently, both by themselves and with mutual friends. They had been married for fifty years now and cared very much for each other, and they usually did things together.

Today, while having breakfast, an idea occurred to Margaret. She realized that the reason Ed thought he heard fine was because she had been his ears for several years now. Every time he would miss something, he would just ask her. She would then repeat it over and over again until he finally understood her. I know what I should do, thought Margaret. I'll find some excuse to not be with him for a whole day. I'm sure that by the end of the day, Ed will be more open to the idea of getting the hearing aid. She made up her mind to put her plan in action.

After breakfast, Margaret made a few phone calls. When she was done, she felt very pleased with the results. She had set up a Saturday morning meeting for her ladies' group at church. After the meeting, they would go out for lunch. She would spend the early afternoon visiting her best friend, and later on, they would both attend a free concert at a local college. Since these activities were all for the ladies, Ed would need to spend the whole day on his own.

90

Margaret informed Ed of her plans for the following Saturday. Ed decided that he, too, would go out in the morning with some friends. He set up a game of golf with Rick, who was his contemporary, and John and Bill, who were much younger but always enjoyed his company.

Saturday came, and, as planned, Margaret went out to her meeting. Before dressing for his golf outing, Ed turned on the radio to check what the weather would be. He heard that it was going to be a sunny day with a high of fifty-four degrees. Ed was a little surprised it would be so cool, but, as far as he was concerned, any weather was good for golf. He made sure he had his heaviest undershirt on and wore his green plaid flannel shirt and his jacket. He did not want to be cold with all that walking. At nine thirty in the morning, he picked up Rick, and they drove to the golf course.

They were enjoying a leisurely game of golf when the conversation turned to gardening. Ed loved taking care of his garden, and was very proud of it. He had a large vegetable garden and many varieties of beautiful flowers. John was talking about a new type of fertilizer he had successfully used in his garden. The two men, though different in ages, had many things in common.

The game took a long time. By noon, Ed had not only taken off his jacket, but was perspiring profusely. "These weather people can never predict the temperature," he complained, wiping the perspiration from his forehead with a handkerchief.

"Well, they didn't do too bad today," responded Rick. "They said a high of eighty-four, and it must already be eighty degrees now. Why on earth did you wear your heavy flannel shirt on a hot day like today?"

Ed thought it better not to respond, and he just tried to concentrate on his shot. He raised his club, swung, and, for the first time in many years, did not make contact with the ball.

While they were waiting for the group ahead of them to finish playing, Bill said, "I had a talk yesterday with my cousin Sylvia— you know her, the stockbroker. She was concerned about her dad. I think GD will die soon. He should go straight up. Such a good guy!"

"Great!" answered Ed.

The three men looked at him with puzzled expressions.

"I think it is a good idea to buy GE," he continued. "You are right that it's a good buy—it's an excellent stock. I agree with you, it should go straight up. Do as you said, and buy it soon."

This time, it was the three friends who thought it better not to explain.

After the game, they stopped for a sandwich and a beer on the way home. After lunch, Ed drove Rick back to his house. Now that the two younger friends were not there, Rick thought it his responsibility to explain to Ed how he'd misunderstood the remark about Sylvia's dad.

Ed's face turned serious. With a grave voice, he said "I hope Bill is not angry at me. I meant no disrespect to his uncle, I just misunderstood."

"Don't worry about it," was his buddy's reply.

Early in the afternoon, Ed decided to call the store that usually took care of his gardening needs. I am going to try that new fertilizer John was talking about this morning, he thought. I always bought another type. I wonder if they carry this one. It's such a hot day that I don't feel like going out and hauling all those ten-pound bags into the car. Luckily enough, they deliver, so if they have it, I'll just order it over the phone. He looked in the phone book and dialed the number.

A new store clerk answered. After talking with him for a few minutes and finding out that they did indeed have what he wanted in stock, Ed placed the order. He thought it was funny that the clerk said "Consider it as done" even before Ed had told him how much he wanted. We'll see, thought Ed. "I would like twenty of them," he requested.

He sensed the surprise at the other end of the line.

"Are you sure you can use that many?" asked the clerk politely. "You know, we don't accept returns if you do not use it."

"Yes, I know. I have been dealing with your store for many years now. I know my gardening needs, so just send me my order, young man."

"If you say so," said the clerk.

"I'll probably be taking a nap by the time your delivery comes," explained Ed, "so just leave it in my backyard."

A few moments later Ed went to his bedroom with a smile on his face. This should take care of my garden, he thought.

At five in the afternoon, Ed woke up from his nap. Thinking that they must have delivered the fertilizer by now, he went to his back door, opened it, and almost fainted. He could not see past the huge mound of bags covering his whole yard. Immediately, he went to the phone. The same person he had talked to before answered. "What kind of a joke is this?" demanded Ed.

"What do you mean, sir?"

"I did not order all that stuff in my backyard!"

"Sorry to contradict you sir, but you did. I even double-checked with you if you wanted twenty, since I told you we only sell them in tons."

Ed stood thoughtfully for a moment, replaying the earlier conversation in his mind, and then silently hung up the phone.

By the time Margaret came back from her outing, Ed had already made an appointment to get his hearing aid the next day.

What Happened to My Home?

I have lived in this neighborhood for a while. I am familiar with all of its surroundings and inhabitants. It is a nice place to raise my kids. I do like it here.

But this afternoon, when I came back home from a long outing, I was shocked to find my beautiful home destroyed. Since we had not had any sort of bad weather, the surprise was even greater.

As I was trying to figure out what had happened, I heard my neighbor Karl saying, "Yes, it was time to cut down that tree. It was too close to the house."

So that was it! Who does he think he is to destroy an honest squirrel's home? I had lived in that tree longer than he has been in that ugly house of his. How would he feel if I destroyed his home? Well, it is time for me to find a better neighborhood!

Who Are You?

I was finishing my breakfast when I heard a scratching at the door. I ignored it for a while, but when it persisted, I got up to investigate. It was a tan dog, medium sized, with beautiful big eyes that seemed to beg me to let him in. I did, and then I realized it was wearing a collar. I bent down and read, "If you find this cat, call this number."

The first thing I did was look for my glasses. I found them on top of the table where I had left them and looked at the animal again. Sure enough, it was a dog, as I had first thought.

I petted him and was ready to call the number on his collar when, in gratitude, he looked at me and gave a thankful meow!

Before I call the animal's owner, I had better make two appointments: one with my eye doctor to change my prescription, and the other with the ear specialist in case it was really a dog.

An Unexpected Response

My name is Mark. I am a single young man of twenty-two. I have a good, steady job, and today I am going to do something I have been wanting to do for a long time.

At lunchtime, I rush to the jewelry store not far from the place where I work. After some deliberation, I select what I want, pay for it, and am told I may pick up the article by the end of the day.

I get back to work very excited. The hours pass, and at six pm I return to the jewelry store. The same salesperson comes to take care of me and, remembering my purchase, smiles, goes to the backroom, and returns with a small box in his hand. He opens the box. I inspect it, tell him it's exactly what I want, and place the box in my coat pocket.

Oh! I can't wait to show Eileen tonight, I think while driving back home. Eileen is my girlfriend. We have been together for a while now. I met her when I was still in college. I did not have any money at the time, and she put up with me being broke and not able to take her anywhere.

Today is Eileen's birthday, and I am taking her to dinner, to a pretty fancy place, to make up for all those times we could not go out before.

It is now eight pm, and we are at the restaurant. Very nice! We have just ordered our favorite meals and are drinking a glass of wine.

"Guess where I went shopping today?" I ask her with a teasing note in my voice.

"I don't have the faintest idea," she answers.

Then I bring out the small box from my coat pocket and, as I do so, I notice her face light up. I open the box in front of her, and as I take out my coveted graduation ring, the one I could not afford to buy when I graduated, I place it on my finger and, smiling, look back at her.

A huge transformation has happened. The face that a moment ago was so happy is now showing signs of repressed anger. Who can understand women? I thought she would be very happy for me to be able to finally wear the school ring that I had wanted for so long. I tell you, women's reactions are beyond my comprehension!

Breaking Point

Theresa sat in front of her desk late at night, thinking. She was upset and did not know what to do. She had been working very hard lately as a waitress at a cafeteria downtown, spending many hours on her feet. Lunchtime was especially difficult. All the people from the offices nearby were in a hurry, and they all wanted to be served right away. She resented the way some of them treated her.

Theresa had managed to finish high school, but that did not seem enough to get her a good job. She had hoped to find work in an office, but she could hardly type, her spelling was terrible, and her math was worse.

Theresa's husband, Peter, was responsible for her current predicament. He worked at the same cafeteria, and was the one who had convinced the manager to hire Theresa. Then, a couple of months ago, when she had said that she needed to get out of that job, Peter had encouraged her to first take a college course with him. He told her it would help her get a better job.

Peter was doing fine with the course, but Theresa was not. And to make things worse, he made fun of how badly she was doing.

Peter enjoyed his work in the cafeteria. He enjoyed going to school in the evenings and learning new things. He had hope for the future. Theresa was just the opposite. Very highly strung, she got upset easily. She resented criticism, and she took Peter's jokes very seriously. From the time she went back to school, things had gone from bad to worse.

Tonight was a good example. Theresa realized that part of it might just be the physical fatigue. By the time she came home, she was so tired that she could barely think straight or communicate. It was almost Greek to her. What do you mean, I made an error? It makes perfect sense to me! She did not understand her mistake and was too tired to try to fix it.

She had never had much patience, and now it was really running out. Peter always accused her of being too impatient. She accused him of gloating whenever he was able to complete an assignment she couldn't. Just another way of making fun of her, she would think. He always denied it, but for her it was a reality.

Theresa sat there, trying to think, but could not clarify her thoughts. She could hear Peter snoring placidly on the bed. How can he go to sleep after all this miscommunication when he knows how difficult things are for me? she thought. Once he fell asleep, it was almost impossible to wake him.

As time passed, Theresa got more and more upset. It must be very late, she thought, and tomorrow I have to get up early. She raised her eyes to the clock on the wall. As she did, she noticed that Peter had left his hammer on top of the kitchen table. How many times had she told him not to do that?

By now, Theresa had a splitting headache. She was getting angrier by the minute. Finally, she could not control herself anymore. In a blind rage, she got up, took the hammer from the table, lifted her arm, and struck the beast with all her strength not once, but two, three times. She heard an awful sound, but she did not care. From now on, she did not have to suffer insults anymore. Tomorrow she would need to explain her actions, but at present, they made her feel much better.

Theresa collapsed, a listless bundle, on the big recliner, the one Peter always used to watch TV. Exhaustion overcame her, and she fell into a dreamless sleep.

As the sun began to rise the next morning, Theresa woke up. Right away, she remembered the awful thing she had done. She silently prayed, with her eyes still closed, that it had all been just a bad dream. Slowly, she opened her eyes and saw the scene in front of her. Peter's body lay still on the bed, as lifeless as it could be. Her eyes filled with tears and remorse as they went to the desk, where Peter's computer lay, the screen broken, with the hammer still next to it.

How am I ever going to explain that to him? she thought.

A Journey of a Hundred "UR"s

Duran Murphy and his friend *Murray Churchill* had been friends for *fourteen* years. They had met *during* their military careers in *Europe*. *Murray's surname* often caused people to remark about his British ancestor, but in reality, he had been born in the United States in a small *rural* town. He felt at home among chickens, *turkeys*, corn, and *turnips*. The *lure* of seeing the world and his desire to be thoroughly *surprised* by it had led him to join the army. He and *Murray* had both *survived* many dangerous situations.

Duran was from an *urban* area. He had a wife, Rita, and *four* children ranging in age from two to eight, while his friend just had a pet *turtle*. *Duran's* parents were of an advanced age and in declining health. His sister *Laura* was a *nurse*, and his other sister, *Maureen*, ran the office of a well-known *surgeon*. Since their brother was away, the *burden* of care fell on the two sisters, who looked after their parents as best they could. The three siblings had recently been talking about moving their parents to a *nursing* home near *Laura's* home.

Both *Duran* and *Murray* were on a *furlough* now. They were *touring* California and especially wanted to visit Big *Sur*. Today was *Thursday* the *fourth*, the day when they would continue their drive. The two friends rose early and met for a *leisurely* cup of coffee at the cafeteria across from the motel, way before the *hour* when the *hurricane* of *four* small children would *hurl* down on them. As the waitress *poured* them cups of steaming brew, a *dour* expression appeared on *Duran's* face. "We have to be very careful how we drive from here on," he said. "There are many sharp *curves* in the road we'll take, and *our current* cargo is my wife and little ones."

His pal gave him a *furtive* look. "You think I'm not a good driver?"

"As far as *your* driving goes, the *jury* is still out," answered his buddy with a smile.

"Whatever you decide is fine with me. I am in no *hurry*. I *sure* don't care if we go as fast as a bullet or if you want to throw *burlap* sacks on a couple of *burros* and ride them down the coast."

Duran heard a noise, *turned* his head, and saw Rita and the children. The kids were running, of *course*.

100

"Careful! Don't *hurt yourselves*" said Rita to the children as she put her *purse* on the table. All the kids threw themselves at their dad and at "Uncle *Murray*," who quickly *lurched* to the side to avoid being squashed.

Their drinks with breakfast were delicious: *pure*, fresh-squeezed orange juice for the children and strong, hot coffee for the adults. The children were very interested in two things: a big *mural* of a beautiful Western landscape painted on one of the walls, and a *burly* man with a *purple turban* on his head. As Bryan, *Duran's* son, *turned* to look at the big man, one of his brothers complained *urgently*, "My toast is almost *burnt!*"

"Carbon can *cure* some digestive problems," answered his dad. He took a piece of toast and, with his knife, brushed away the black on it. "See, here is *your* bread. You can clean the other one."

After finishing breakfast, they all piled into the big *durable* SUV, its engine *purring* like a happy cat.

The scenery along the road was beautiful. "This is *nature* at its best!" said Rita. Below was the Pacific Ocean, today a deep *turquoise* color. The *fury* of its huge waves did not keep many young *surfers* from enjoying themselves.

Nancy, the oldest child, was writing in her *journal* about all the new places they had seen in the *course* of their trip. She had already filled *fourteen* pages. Her mom referred to her as "*our* writer" only half in jest, since she thought Nancy would *surely* be a writer when she grew up.

"What a beautiful place!" said Nancy in wonder and admiration at the sight of the seagulls and all the *furry creatures* in their *natural* environment.

After they had driven for several *hours*, a *curtain* of fog appeared, blocking their view of the ocean. "I *surrender*! Let's not drive any *further* for now," said *Duran*. "Time to stop for lunch. Who is ready for *hamburgers*?"

"Me!" replied *four* young voices in unison.

"I'm glad that, because of this fog, the car won't be hot as a *furnace* when we *return*," said Rita. "We are lucky that we won't have to *burn ourselves*."

Duran found a good parking spot, and the whole group of adults and *urchins pursued* the demands of their empty stomachs.

101

It Was Nice Working With You

I am glad it is Friday so that I can rest the whole weekend, I think as I get up from my desk and walk toward the exit.

Mr. Jacobs, my boss, is leaving at the same time as me. I have been working for this company for twenty years, and for him for the last year. He is the best boss I have ever had, very nice and friendly.

As our paths cross on the way to the elevator, he says with a smile, "It was nice working with you, Bill."

"Oh, no!" I answer, sad to see my favorite boss go away. "Are you leaving the company?"

"No, I'm not, but you are," is his answer.

Have I told you lately how much I hate my horrible boss?

Don't Look Behind You

As we were walking in a meadow next to a winding river in the countryside, my boyfriend Paul said to me, "Don't look behind you."

Why do people say that? What did he expect me to do after such a warning? Of course, I turned my head to see, and I saw what I was not supposed to. I have to admit that the instant I looked, I regretted not having followed the advice. Behind us was a gigantic bull.

I don't have any problems with cows, but an enormous bull is a very different story. Those huge horns don't make me feel very safe. To make things worse, I was dressed in red. As everyone knows, red is said to make bulls angry and ready to charge. Being chased by a bull had been the farthest thing from my mind when I selected my outfit that morning, or I would have chosen whichever color makes a bull stay put and not move a muscle. (Which color is that? you may ask. I don't know, but I'm sure my good friend Google would have been happy to tell me.)

From the start, I did not like the look in the animal's eyes. They seemed to be saying to me, "Aha, an easy target!" I was not able to hold his intense stare, so I turned my head around. Before my brain had even given the command, my legs started to move at a very rapid pace. That only made the bull think that I was fair game, and it came after me. Paul, who would have preferred to ignore the bull, had to follow suit and ran beside me.

I think that bull must have been training for the summer Olympics, or at least for the running of the bulls in Pamplona. There was no way that we could outrun it. Little by little, it gained on us until we could almost feel its agitated, furious breath on our necks. There was only one thing to do. I climbed the closest tree, and Paul followed suit. I've never been a good climber but it is amazing what a little incentive like a crazy bull behind you can do.

Up in the tree, we waited in the hope that the bull would eventually get bored and leave, but this was no ordinary animal, I tell you. Not only was he an Olympic athlete, but he also had the persistence of a research scientist. He kept looking at us, making a guttural threatening noise and butting his horns against the trunk

103

of the tree. Thank God that climbing trees was not his favorite sport.

There we waited for at least an hour until we realized that our foe must have won a gold medal for single-mindedness. He was not moving away. The only recourse we had was our mobile phones. I dialed 911.

Can you imagine trying to explain to the person on the other end of the line that this is not a joke, that we have indeed been pursued by a bull and are not figuratively but literally up a tree? It took several tries for them to take me seriously. Once that had happened, I had trouble explaining where we were, in the middle of nowhere. Luckily for us, they were able to locate us from my phone's signal, and they called the nearest farm owner.

It took a long time for the farmer to come. Finally, he appeared. How foolish did I feel when, seeing the bull, the old farmer said, "Maggie, I've been looking for you everywhere! This time you really strayed far."

Our ferocious bull turned out to be Maggie, his cow! As soon as she obediently and meekly followed him, we were able to come down from our perch. Paul and I made a pact right then and there that if this story ever came out, we would convert Maggie into Ivan the fierce bull, so I beg you to please keep our secret.

Alphabet Short Story

As far as I am concerned, said young Lucy,
Boys are a bore—yes, I say it again, a bore.
Children still, even when in high school.
Dim witted as far as understanding girls.
Even the most intelligent ones do not have a clue what a girl wants.
Football, other sports, and cars are the only thoughts on their minds.
Going places just with their friends.
Home for them is their peer group.
Imagination they are lacking, as far as how to treat a girl.
Just when I think Mark is beginning to care for me, I find this:
Keys to a car is his only dream.
Long have I known him, ever since elementary school.
Many times we've gotten together.
Never for anything romantic.
Only to study or watch TV.
Perhaps he's gotten too used to me.
Questions I've asked many times, but he just smiles and does not answer,
Resulting in my never knowing what he is thinking.
Since people see us together,
They assume he is my boyfriend.
Unless I tell them otherwise,
Very few people know we are just friends.
What should I do?
X-mas is coming.
Yuletide celebrations, and all.
Zombie-like he will probably stay. I'd better call my girlfriend!

Castles in the Air

Chapter 1: Connecting

He lay on the sand, his blond hair disheveled by the warm ocean breeze. Oh, how he loved that unmistakable aroma of the sea! His hands played with the sand, a fort taking shape under them, while his mind played with the idea that had occurred to him the previous night. He stayed there for a long time, absorbed in his thoughts. Finally, when the sun began to descend, he got up, shook the sand from his body, and muttered to himself in a pleased voice, "It might work!"

He entered the oceanfront hotel where he was staying and asked for the key to his room. The clerk gave him the key, said, "Mr. Deskin, a message arrived for you while you were at the beach," and handed Tom a piece of paper. It read, "Intrigued by your call, can't wait to talk to you. You can reach me at home after 6:30 pm." The note was signed "Rebecca."

Tom walked towards the row of elevators and looked at his watch. It was already 7:00 pm. I'll contact Rebecca and set up a dinner date before taking a shower, he thought. I hope she hasn't had her dinner yet.

He got to his room and went directly to the phone. "Please connect me with 258-2910," he said. The hotel operator dialed the number. Tom had heard only two rings when a pleasant female voice answered.

"Hello?"

Tom said, "Rebecca, this is Tom. I would love to take you out to dinner at eight tonight, that is, if you have not already eaten."

"That would be fine, Tom. I just got home. I was afraid I'd miss your call. There was a huge accident on the highway, and the traffic came to a halt until they cleared it."

"OK," said Tom, smiling to himself. "I'll pick you up at a quarter to eight." Off to a good start, he thought.

At exactly 7:45 pm, Tom arrived at Rebecca's condominium. Punctuality was one of his good qualities. He rang the bell while adjusting his tie with the other hand. It had been a long time since he had last seen Rebecca. They had both attended the same college and had even dated occasionally while in school. Will she have changed? Tom wondered.

Just then, the door opened, and a slim figure appeared. Rebecca was even more beautiful than Tom had remembered. Her dark brown hair cascaded to her shoulders. Her eyes were an unusual gray-green color and had such a special brightness to them that they reminded him of two shining stars in a dark summer sky. He had never seen eyes so beautiful.

"You look gorgeous," Tom said, giving her a kiss on the cheek.

"So do you," she responded unabashedly as she returned the kiss. It was true: in his dark blue suit and red tie, or even in less formal attire, Tom was indeed a very handsome man.

They arrived at the restaurant and, at Tom's request, were seated at a table away from the more crowded areas. They had a leisurely drink and then ordered dinner. The waiter placed the food in front of them, assured himself that everything was as it should be, and walked away.

As soon as they were alone, Tom said, "I have a proposition for you, Rebecca. Please hear me out completely before making up your mind. If, after hearing all the details, you don't want any part of it, just say so. I won't try to convince you. I'll just find another partner. I already have someone else in mind, though I admit I would prefer if it were you. I only ask that you hear me out, and that, if you decide not to participate, you forget what I'm about to tell you. By the way, I'll deny having ever said anything about this matter. Agreed?"

Rebecca gave him a puzzled look. "You've got me curious now, Tom. What are you talking about?"

"You'll never know unless you agree to those terms."

Rebecca's expression turned serious. She thought for a moment, then said, "OK, Tom, I agree. You may begin."

107

Tom took a sip of his coffee and began.

Chapter 2: The Plan

"I've always thought that I could do much better than my job at Morris & Johnson," said Tom. "Some people would call me a dreamer, but I do know my strong points as well as my shortcomings."

Rebecca was tempted to say, "Do you have any shortcomings?" but decided not to interrupt him.

"I'll tell you the truth, Rebecca, I feel like time is running out for me. I am twenty-seven years old, and I have not yet found my niche in life. That is, until now. Last night I was lying in bed, thinking of how I'm wasting my life in that dead-end job of mine and how I'll probably end up like my old man, who died prematurely and without a penny... when I had what I think is a terrific idea. If everything works as I've planned, and I don't see why it shouldn't, in a few months you and I could both be extremely wealthy."

That last phrase caught Rebecca's attention. Not that she didn't have any money, not at all: her annual salary would have been considered excellent by most people. But she was not like most people.

Rebecca had very expensive tastes. As a child, she had been spoiled by both her mother, a highly regarded real estate agent, and her father, a medical doctor with a very lucrative practice. They had divorced when Rebecca was six. Rebecca had spent Sundays and summers with her dad and the rest of the time with her mom. Her parents dueled for their daughter's affection in the only manner they knew how: by showering her with expensive gifts, each trying to outshine the other. She had learned very early in life how to work their failed marriage to her benefit. As a result, she always had everything she'd ever dreamed of, and even some things she really didn't, but one parent or the other had thought it might do the trick of bringing her unconditionally to their side.

Rebecca heard Tom say, "Human beings love to dream. Even the most practical men and women succumb at times, in the privacy of their thoughts, to a little daydreaming. I have decided to give people what they want. If they like to build castles in the air, I'll give them the most enticing castles they have ever seen. In the process, you and I will build our own, firm, foundation on the ground, castles for ourselves. It goes like this:

"Many people, myself included, come to this beautiful place for a vacation. Here we can enjoy not only the beach, but also casinos, the best plays, symphony concerts, and more. It occurred to me that when people are on vacation, they are not their usual cautious selves. One lives a little more in a make-believe world. One is more apt to chat and strike up a friendship with a stranger. Having left behind one's friends and responsibilities leaves more room for new friends, for adventure, and even for risk taking.

"I will move from the hotel where I am currently staying to another one, and you will come with me. I will pose as Mr. Joseph Streemer, a well-established businessman who has inherited his father's enormous fortune after the untimely death of Mr. Streemer Sr. You will be Miss Jennifer Johns, my efficient, devoted personal assistant, whose love for her boss is obvious to everyone except the object of her affection."

On hearing this, Rebecca's lips formed a smile and her complexion turned pink.

"My place of business is in New York," Tom continued, "but I come here often with the dual purpose of relaxing from my very busy schedule while at the same time supervising my business ventures in the area. For Miss Johns, it is a paid vacation with just a little work thrown in. Are you with me so far?"

"Yes," said Rebecca. "Please go on."

"As soon as I find a likely candidate, I will point them out to you. You will make sure to 'happen' to be wherever they usually spend part of their day and to start a casual conversation. I know you have inherited your mother's knack for pleasant conversation and for placing ideas into peoples' heads without them being aware of it."

109

Rebecca did not like hearing this, but she had to agree that it was true, so she did not respond.

"You will casually mention to them that you are here at the request of your employer, the well-known, handsome Mr. Joseph Streemer, whose fortune you dream of sharing one day. You will emphasize the wealth, business acumen, and social standing of your boss, but you will leave vague the nature of his business.

"We will wait a few days for your new friendship to blossom. Then, just when they are dying to meet the famous Mr. Streemer, I'll make my appearance. I will be a very pleasant, down-to-earth person, generous to a fault, always buying rounds of drinks for my newfound friends. I will never speak of my wealth, but my actions will speak louder than any words. In their presence, I will remind you of business calls, of business ventures to be checked, and such. I will casually drop some of the most well-known names in the social and business circles. After a short time, they will be so impressed with me that, wanting to prove that they, too, are successful people, they will take the bait.

"One day I will appear distracted. When asked, I will explain that a business deal that I was planning with a very good friend had fallen through: I just got word that my friend had been in a car accident. The doctors say he will recover completely, but it will take a few weeks. Our business opportunity needed immediate action. I feel bad for him, losing that opportunity. It would have made him financially independent from his stepfather, with whom he does not get along too well. I know there will be other opportunities I can share with him in the future, but one has to wait until the right one comes along. For myself too, I hate to see such a gold mine go untapped, but I happen to have my money tied up in so many other things at present that I cannot do this all by myself.

"They will ask for more details about the business venture, and I will tell them that even though it involves a certain amount of risk, it is a relatively safe proposition. The return will be from twice to ten times the investment, the waiting time simply one year. They will be so willing to get into it! They will begin thinking, right away, what they'll do with the money they'll make. They will beg me to take them in as partners. I'll hesitate, talk again about the risk. I'll ask them if they can afford the off chance of a failure. Only when they have assured me that yes, they can afford to lose their investment, will I agree. We will close our verbal agreement with a drink. The next day, we will sign some phony documents, and the money will transfer hands.

"We will approach all the people I consider to be likely candidates. I don't want to boast, but I am a very good judge of character. Simply by observing a person, without even talking to them, I can tell you a lot about them. I always felt I would have made an excellent psychologist.

"I will resign from my job, telling them that I had a much better offer while on vacation here and am planning to stay. You will do the same. We will devote our efforts full time to this scheme. In a few months, we will have enough money to leave the country and enjoy our newly acquired wealth. If you prefer, we could then reassume our real identities. Our lives will be a dream: all the pleasures money can buy, with no work involved."

Rebecca realized how much like Tom it was to have gone directly into his business proposition without even asking her anything about herself. At one point in her life, in her first year in college, she'd had a crush on Tom, but those days were over. Now all they could be was business partners.

After a long period of silence, Rebecca spoke. "Tom, I always knew you had a very fertile mind. I'm still not completely sure if this is the right thing for me to do, but I'll go along with your plan."

"I'm glad." Tom raised his glass and said, "Rebecca Fields, to our partnership! I knew you would accept, and I know you won't regret your decision."

I wonder, thought Rebecca.

Chapter 3: The Execution

The day after their talk, Tom and Rebecca took rooms in another oceanfront hotel. After a few days there, Tom pointed out to Rebecca Mr. and Mrs. John Tremont, their first targets. It was, in effect, very easy for Rebecca to strike up a conversation with them.

The Tremonts seemed to be a friendly middle-aged couple. Rebecca followed Tom's instructions to the letter. Every day she got together with the Tremonts for different activities. Anybody looking at them would have assumed they were old and dear friends. From afar, day after day, Tom watched and smiled, sure in the knowledge that his scheme was moving along exactly as planned. When Tom felt the time was right, he came into the picture.

One day, while cooling off after a game of tennis with the Tremonts, he caught himself thinking, "Rebecca can be so charming!"

Precisely at the same moment, the same thought was going through Rebecca's mind. "Tom sure can charm anyone. He has these people eating from the palms of his hands."

The scheme worked exactly as planned. In a few days the couple was ready for the "bait." They took it with no hesitation. Tom had to try hard not to laugh while their conversation took place. He could have predicted, word for word, everything that was said. A couple of days later, the phony papers were signed, and the money changed hands.

Both Tom and Rebecca were very pleased. They celebrated with a special dinner that night. Tom was too absorbed in their victory to notice that her eyes did not seemed as bright that evening.

Chapter 4: The End

The next day was the last one of Mr. and Mrs. Tremont's vacation, so the four of them decided to have lunch together. All during lunch Tom was thinking how well his first job as a con man had gone. I have found the right profession, he thought. I have to hand it to Rebecca too; she is a natural for the job. A few more jobs like this, and I can retire with enough money to last me a lifetime. The first thing I'll buy is that sports car I've always wanted...

Tom's thoughts were interrupted as Mr. Tremont raised his glass and said, "I'd like to drink to friendships, to opportunities taken, to jobs well done. Here I was, enjoying a few days of rest, glad to get away from my job. I did not expect to mix my vacation with business, but the opportunity came along, and I'm very glad I took it." As Tom began to raise his glass, Mr. Tremont said the terrible words. "Mr. Deskin, you are under arrest. Please read him his rights, Agent Fields."

Tom could hardly believe Mr. Tremont's next words. "Rebecca and I have been trying for a long time to make this area a safer place for tourists. I'll make sure she gets a promotion out of this."

Tom looked at Rebecca, who was saying her part. For the first time, he saw that sadness in her beautiful eyes.

Love at First Sight

Every afternoon, you could find him with a friend in the park. He was blond, well built, just the right weight for his height, and with stunning blue eyes—definitely very good looking. People noticed him wherever he went.

This particular afternoon, Mary left work early. She had been working as a secretary for Miller & Richardson for several years. Today had been her last day. Times were bad, and they needed to economize, so they let her go. She was sad and vulnerable.

Mary sat on a bench opposite from him, and right away, he stole her heart. She forgot all about her troubles. She just felt a strong desire to be close to him.

Through a mutual friend, she learned that his name was Sam Butler. His life had been difficult from the start. Both his parents had died in a car accident shortly after he was born, and he had no other relatives, no family at all.

The next day Mary could not help coming back to the park, hoping to see Sam again. There he was. They looked at each other, and he smiled at her. Mary thought of her husband Joe. Joe was not handsome, but he was a good man. They had been married for five years. They did not have any children: they had tried but finally discovered they could not conceive. They had told each other it was probably better that way.

Day after day, Mary came back to the park. The more she got to know Sam, the more she felt in love with him. At times, sitting on that bench, Mary would observe his eyes filling with tears. She wanted so much to make them disappear with a kiss! Mary noticed that he did not seem to mind drinking in front of people. He seemed oblivious to the rest of the world, but he soon developed a strong attachment to her.

Until she met Sam, Mary had felt happy in her marriage. Now, she realized that it was not enough. Finally, after a few weeks, once she was sure of their feelings, she decided to confront Joe and tell him about Sam.

She was very surprised by her husband's reaction. He simply said that if it would make her happy, he would sign the papers. She had expected more opposition than that!

The following day, Mary and Joe went to set their decision in motion. When the clerk came to help them, Mary's face lit up as she said, "We've come to begin the process of adopting baby Sam Butler."

Writing: Between Torture and Fun

Even though I usually go for the fun part of writing, I realize that for serious writers who have deadlines to deal with and who depend on their writing for their sustenance, writing can, at times, be torture.

There are instances when I feel the need to write to give expression to some thought or feeling inside me. Then writing pours out, like a summer shower, fast and sometimes furious, fingers hitting the keyboard as quickly as possible before the thoughts fade away. Other times, I write just for fun, starting with an idea, phrase, or prompt and letting it lead me wherever it wants. On those occasions, I am often the most surprised at the direction the story takes me. In contrast, other times I know exactly where I want to end and try very carefully to get there by any devious way I can. All I can say is that in all of the above cases, I enjoy writing. I am grateful that I am able to write just for fun and not for a living.

About the Author

Lidia Hidalgo, originally from Cuba, is a retired college professor of math and computer skills.

She lives in Rocky River, Ohio and has been a member of the Rocky River Senior Center's writing group for several years, where she is known for the surprising twist endings in her stories.

Lidia enjoys writing both serious and lighthearted very short stories. Most of the stories in this collection originated in ten-minute writing exercises at her writing group.

Made in the USA
Lexington, KY
22 December 2017